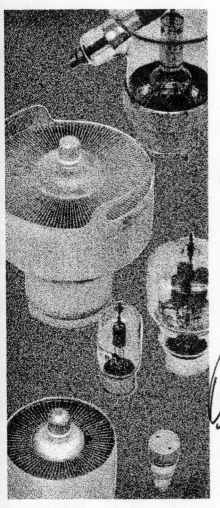

CARE
AND FEEDING
OF
POWER GRID TUBES

PREPARED BY LABORATORY STAFF,
VARIAN, EIMAC DIVISION

VARIAN, EIMAC DIVISION
301 INDUSTRIAL WAY
SAN CARLOS, CALIFORNIA 94070

CARE AND FEEDING OF POWER GRID TUBES

THIRD PRINTING 1978

LIBRARY OF CONGRESS NO. 67-30070

TABLE OF CONTENTS

LIST OF ILLUSTRATIONS

SECTION 1

INTRODUCTION

This handbook analyzes the operation of EIMAC power grid tubes and provides design and application information to assist the user of these tubes to achieve long tube life, maximum operating efficiency and circuit stability consistent with the full tube capability.

THE CARE AND FEEDING OF POWER GRID TUBES has been prepared in answer to thousands of questions asked of the EIMAC engineering and laboratory staff over a period of years. Data contained in this volume represents the combined efforts of these staff members to provide meaningful information on all phases of the design of equipment using power grid tubes, and the techniques recommended for the application of power grid tubes in modern circuits.

EIMAC transmitting tubes are recommended for new equipment design and for replacement of older triode, tetrode and pentode tubes in the redesign of older equipment. Compact EIMAC tubes feature reduced internal coupling between input and output circuits, low internal inductance and capacitance, improved linearity and high operating efficiency. EIMAC tubes are built for long operating life and are rated for use well into the VHF region (and in the case of the external anode tetrodes and pentodes, well into the UHF region). EIMAC tubes are designed to withstand electrical and physical abuse and can operate under extreme environmental conditions. The high power gain and excellent efficiency of EIMAC tubes permits design of equipments that operate with a minimum of drive power, allowing a minimum number of stages to achieve the desired power level.

Circuit design and application information in this book are applicable to all EIMAC power grid tubes. For specific ratings, operating parameters and information dealing with particular tube types, refer to the technical data sheet and the Product Test Specification sheet for the tube in question. The data sheet is generally supplied with the tube. Designers of new equipment are urged to use the Test Specification as well as the data sheet. The Test Specification sheet shows the limits on the range of the more important tube characteristics. Free copies of the data sheet or the Test Specification may be obtained upon request to: Power Grid Product Manager, Varian, EIMAC Division, 301 Industrial Way, San Carlos, California, U.S.A., 94070 or Varian A.G., Postfach, Grienbachstrasse 17, 6300 Zug, Switzerland.

For further technical information, contact EIMAC or your nearest Varian field sales office, listed on the inside rear cover of this publication.

SECTION 2
WHAT IS A POWER GRID TUBE?

A power grid tube is a device utilizing the flow of free electrons in a vacuum. It has an emitting surface called the cathode, and one or more grids controlling the flow of electrons. An element called the anode collects the electrons. EIMAC manufactures gridded tubes which handle large amounts of power, as contrasted to receiving type tubes; hence, the term "Power Grid Tubes."

All gridded tubes must have a cathode and an anode. The general class of tube as described by the terms "triode," "tetrode," and "pentode" is determined by the total number of elements within the tube envelope. Therefore, these terms also indicate the number of grids. A triode has one grid, a tetrode has two grids, and a pentode has three grids.

2.1   TRIODES

The total current flow from the cathode of a three-electrode tube is determined by the electrostatic field near the cathode. The electrostatic field is a function of Ec, the grid to cathode potential, and Eb/μ, the potential due to the plate voltage electrostatic flux penetrating between the grid wires. The "μ", or amplification factor, is a characteristic of a triode which in turn is a function of the physical size and location of the grid structure.

The total cathode current of an ideal triode can be determined by the equation

$$I_k = K \left(E_c + \frac{E_b}{\mu} \right)^{3/2}$$

I_k = cathode current

K = a constant determined by tube dimensions

E_c = grid voltage

E_b = plate voltage

μ = amplification factor of tube

One of the more important parameters of a triode is the amplification factor or "μ". The μ of a triode can be determined from the equation

$$\mu = \frac{\Delta E_b}{\Delta E_c} \quad \text{with the plate current held constant}$$

ΔE_b = change in plate voltage

ΔE_c = change in grid voltage

EIMAC manufactures triodes with μ values ranging from 5 to 200. The low μ tubes are generally used in audio service or any application which requires a large change in plate current without driving the tube into the positive grid region. The difference between a tube with a μ of 12 and one with a μ of 20 can be seen by comparing Figure 1 to Figure 2.

Observe how much more plate current at a given plate voltage can be obtained from the 304TL without driving the grid into the positive grid region. Note how much more bias voltage is required for the 304TL to cut the plate current off at some given plate voltage. With this increased bias there is a corresponding increase in grid voltage swing to drive up to the zero grid voltage point on the curve. Low μ tubes have lower voltage gain by definition, and this fact can be seen by comparing Figure 1 and Figure 2.

Low μ tubes also are an excellent choice for series pass tubes in a voltage regulator. They operate over a wide range of load current (pass tube plate current) with low plate voltage drop.

4

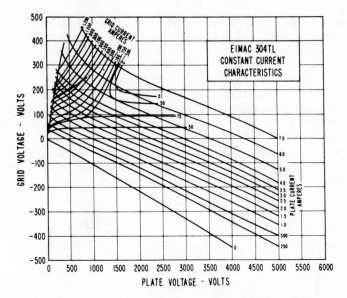

Figure 1. Constant current characteristics of a triode with a μ of 12.

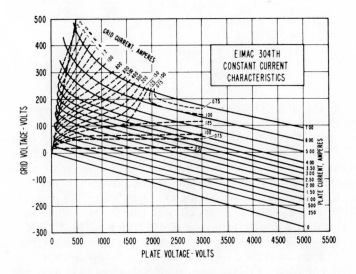

Figure 2. Constant current characteristics of a triode with a μ of 20.

The medium μ (20-50) triodes are generally used in radio frequency amplifiers and oscillators. They are also good audio amplifiers and modulators.

The high μ (200) triodes have been designed so that the operating bias is zero (See Figure 3). EIMAC has developed a line of "zero-bias" triodes with plate dissipation ratings of from 400 to 10,000 watts. The "zero-bias" triode is an excellent choice for grounded-grid radio frequency and audio frequency amplifiers. The main advantages are power gain and circuit simplicity. No bias supply is required. No protection circuits for loss of bias or drive are required.

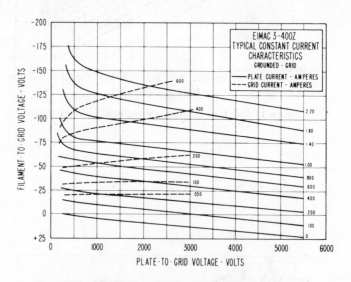

Figure 3. A typical set of grounded-grid constant current curves for a zero-bias triode with a μ of 200.

Low and medium μ rather than high μ tubes are usually preferred for industrial heating applications, such as simple oscillators constructed for induction and dielectric heating. The low-to-medium μ tubes are preferred because of the wide variation in load that an industrial heating oscillator normally works into. Low and medium μ triodes have a much lower grid current variation with the changing load. The grid current of a triode with a μ of 20 will rise far less than the grid current of a triode with a μ of 40 under no load conditions. Very high μ triode oscillators can be designed but extra consideration must be given to the grid current rise under the no load condition. EIMAC has developed a line of triodes specifically for industrial heating applications. These tubes have rugged mounting flanges and flexible filament leads for ease of mounting in the circuit. The tubes are available with water cooling or forced air cooling. The filament structures are large with adequate cathode emission. The grid structures are ruggedly constructed with ample dissipation capability. The grid must be rugged for industrial heating triodes because of the wide variations in load. As the load decreases the grid dissipation increases. A good industrial triode must therefore be capable of operating with a reasonably wide range of load variations.

Most of the triodes manufactured by EIMAC are cylindrically symmetrical. That is, the filament or cathode structure, the grid, and the anode are all cylindrical in shape and are mounted with the axis of each cylinder along the center line of the tube. Some triodes are manufactured with the cathode, grid and anode in the shape of a flat surface. The triodes so constructed are called "Planar" triodes (see Figure 4). This construction technique is necessary to provide very small spacings between the elements, and to achieve very short lead lengths within the tube. The very close spacings are necessary to reduce electron transit time* and therefore allow the tube to be used at frequencies up to 3 GHz and higher. The short leads also increase the operating frequency by reducing lead inductance. Planar triodes are normally used in radio frequency amplifiers in both the continuous wave and pulse modes. The 3CX100A5 and 8755 series triodes are representative of this type of tube. The contacting surfaces of the planar triode tubes are arranged for ease of design into coaxial and waveguide resonators.

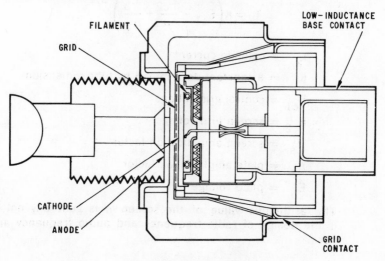

Figure 4. Internal configuration of a planar triode.

*See Section 6.8(d)

2.2 BEAM TETRODE

The tetrode is a four-element tube with two grids. The control grid serves the same purpose as the grid in a triode while a second grid with the same number of bars as the control grid is mounted between the control grid and the anode. The grid bars of the second grid are mounted behind the control grid bars as observed from the cathode surface. Careful alignment of the grids is necessary to assure beam tetrode performance. The additional grid serves as a shield, or screen, between the input circuit and the output circuits of the tetrode, and is called a "screen grid." In addition to serving as a shield, the screen is the accelerating element attracting the electrons from the cathode. The total current from the cathode of a four-element tube is determined by the electrostatic field near the cathode, just as in the triode. The electrostatic field is a function of E_{c1}, the grid to cathode potential, and E_{c2}/μ_s, the potential due to the screen voltage electrostatic flux penetrating through the control grid wires. The plate voltage also contributes a small amount in the ratio of E_b/μ_p; μ_p is usually so large in value that the plate voltage contribution is negligible. In an ideal tetrode there will be no plate current change with a change in plate voltage. A tetrode is therefore a constant current device. The screen voltage and control grid voltage determine the amount of plate current that will flow.

The total cathode current of an ideal tetrode can be obtained by the equation

$$I_k = K\left(E_{c1} + \frac{E_{c2}}{\mu_s} + \frac{E_b}{\mu_p} \right)^{3/2}$$

I_k = cathode current

K = a constant determined by tube dimensions

E_{c1} = control grid voltage

E_{c2} = screen grid voltage

μ_s = screen amplification factor

μ_p = plate amplification factor

E_b = plate voltage

The arithmetic value of the screen μ is generally not used in the design of radio frequency and audio frequency amplifiers.

In most tetrode applications the screen amplification factor is useful to roughly categorize the performance to be expected.

The main advantages of a tetrode over a triode are:

a. Internal plate-to-grid feedback is much lower due to the shielding effect of the screen grid.
b. Tetrodes permit the design of amplifier stages which can operate with driving power less than one per cent of the output power in most cases, and with negligible driving power in many audio applications.
c. Tetrodes operate efficiently and with good life at audio and radio frequencies, including the VHF region (30 to 300 MHz) and in some cases into the UHF region (300 to 3000 MHz).
d. Tetrodes allow designers to build compact, simple, flexible equipment with little spurious radiation.
e. Tetrodes permit the designer to build linear amplifiers with low inter-modulation distortion products. (See Section 4.)

In designing equipment using power grid tubes, consideration must be given to unwanted electron emission from the control and screen grids. The grid materials will emit electrons as a primary emitter if the work function of the grid surface material is low enough. The grid must be at a sufficiently high temperature to emit electrons. Primary grid emission is usually quite low in a thoriated tungsten filament type tube, because grid materials can be used which have high work functions. Also, the work function normally does not change significantly during the life of the tube. In the case of the oxide cathode emitter, the grid materials find themselves in a totally different environment. During the life of the tube, free barium evaporates from the cathode coating material. The rate of evaporation is a function of time and cathode temperature. Some of the free barium finds its way to the control and screen grids, and thus the grid can then become another emitting surface. The hotter the grid, the more emission. Grids are often gold plated to reduce the amount of primary emission.

Another type of grid emission is secondary emission from the screen grid. The screen grid is operated at a relatively low potential, which is necessary to accelerate the electrons emitted from the cathode. Not all of the electrons pass through the screen grid on the way to the plate: some electrons are intercepted by the screen grid. In the process of striking the screen grid, other low energy electrons are emitted, and are called "secondary electrons." If these secondary electrons feel a stronger attraction by the screen, they will fall back into the screen. If, however, they find themselves out in the region between the screen grid and the plate, there is a very good chance that the much higher plate potential will attract them. The result is an electron flow from screen to anode. The control grid is not in this region and so has virtually no control over the number of secondary electrons flowing. During any part of the operating cycle of the tube it is possible that more electrons will leave the screen grid than will arrive. If this occurs, a d-c current meter will indicate a reverse electron flow. On the other hand, if more electrons on the average are arriving than are leaving the screen grid, then the d-c screen meter will indicate a forward electron flow. Reverse screen electron flow is quite normal for high power tetrodes. **The circuit designer must provide a low impedance path for the reverse electron flow.** EIMAC normally states on the data sheet the amount of bleeding current that must be provided from the screen power supply to counteract the emission current (see Figures 5, 6 and 7). If the screen power supply impedance is too high in the **reverse** electron flow direction, the screen voltage will attempt to rise to the plate voltage. Note the emphasis on low impedance in the **reverse** electron flow direction. Most regulated power supplies are low-impedance in the forward electron flow direction only. If the supply is not well bled, the reverse electrons will try to flow from anode to cathode in the regulator series pass tube. As the screen voltage rises, the secondary and plate currents increase, and the tube is in a runaway condition.

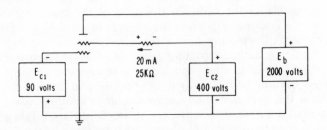

Figure 5. Incorrect screen circuit for tube requiring low impedance screen supply.

OBSERVATION

Assume that at some time during the tube's operating cycle, the reverse electron flow is 20 mA. The voltage drop across the 25 KΩ resistor will be 500 volts. Note the polarities. The effective screen-to-cathode voltage will be 900 volts. The increased screen voltage will increase the secondary emission.

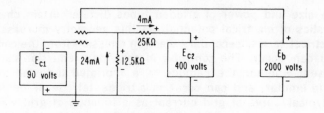

Figure 6. A correct screen circuit for tube requiring low impedance screen supply.

OBSERVATION

By the addition of a 12.5 KΩ resistor from screen to ground, there will be a path for the grid emission 20 mA electron flow.

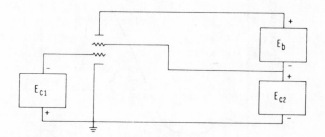

Figure 7. Another approach to swamping the screen circuit.

OBSERVATION

In the circuit of Figure 7, the plate current flows through the screen power supply, swamping the screen power supply. The screen power supply must carry the normal screen and plate current. This scheme is used quite extensively in circuits where the screen is operated at d-c ground. The plate to cathode voltage is the sum of the E_b and E_{c2} power supplies.

The circuit designer must also consider the impedance of the control grid circuit. Primary grid emission can cause trouble if the grid circuit has too high an impedance. Primary grid emission, in the case of oxide cathode tubes, will increase with tube life.

The size and power of gridded tubes dictate certain characteristics of electrical potential. As this geometry increases in electrical terms, secondary electron emission from the control grid can occur. The control grid secondary emission can be present whether the cathode is a thoriated tungsten or an oxide emitter, and can occur in a triode, tetrode or pentode. A typical curve of grid current as a function of grid voltage for a high power thoriated tungsten filament tetrode is shown in Figure 8.

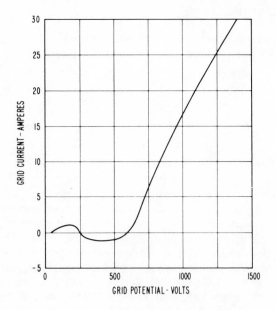

Figure 8. Typical curve of grid current as a function of control grid voltage for a high power thoriated tungsten filament tetrode.

OBSERVATION

In Figure 8, grid current decreases and eventually takes a reverse direction as the grid voltage increases. This reduction and reversal of grid current can be explained by the normal secondary emission characteristics of the metals used in the grid structure. In Figure 9 we see the secondary characteristics of the common metals presented in curve form, giving the ratio of secondary-to-primary electron current as a function of the primary electron potential.

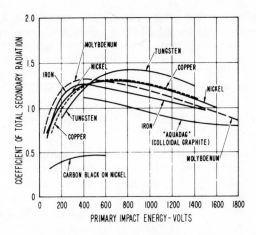

Figure 9. Secondary-emission characteristics of the metals under ordinary conditions. The curve shows the ratio of the number of secondary to primary electrons for various primary-electron impact velocities expressed in volts. (**After Harries.**)

OBSERVATION

A study of Figure 9 shows the region between 200 and 600 volts to be a rather critical one as far as secondary emission is concerned. Any power grid tube which normally operates with 200 to 600 volts on the grid can exhibit the negative resistance characteristic of decreasing grid current with increasing grid voltage when another electrode, such as the anode in a triode or the screen grid in a tetrode, is at a sufficiently high potential to attract the emitted electrons. A driver stage which works into such a non-linear load normally must be designed in such a manner as to tolerate this condition. One technique would be to swamp the driver so that the change in load due to secondary grid emission is a small percentage of the total load the driver works into.

2.3   PENTODES

The pentode is a five-electrode tube; it has three grids. The control grid and screen grids perform the same function as that in the tetrode. The third grid, the suppressor grid, is mounted in the region between the screen grid and the anode. The suppressor grid produces a potential minimum in the plate-screen space. This potential minimum prevents secondary electrons from being interchanged between screen and plate.

Following the analogy with the tetrode tube, the electrostatic field at the surface of the cathode is proportional to the plate voltage in a pentode.

The plate voltage in a pentode has even less effect on the total space current than in the tetrode. The same total space current equation holds:

$$I_k = K \left(E_{cl} + \frac{E_{c2}}{\mu s} \right)^{3/2}$$

The suppressor grid may be operated negative or positive with respect to the cathode, and may be operated at cathode potential. It is possible to control the plate current by means of adjusting the suppressor grid potential. Because of this characteristic, it is possible to amplitude modulate an amplifier by applying the modulating voltage to the suppressor grid. The modulating power will be quite low because of the very low electron interception of the typical suppressor grid.

The main advantages of a pentode are:

 a. Secondary emission effects reduced.
 b. An approach to better linearity when used in linear amplifier service.
 c. It is possible to swing the plate voltage below the screen voltage without exceeding screen dissipation. This characteristic sometimes allows slightly higher power output for a given plate voltage.

Since the suppressor grid reduces the effects of secondary emission, screen grid power supply requirement to provide a reverse electron flow path may be reduced. The screen current requirement for a pentode may be somewhat higher than that for a tetrode of the same general characteristics; control grid power supply requirements will be the same as outlined for tetrodes.

2.4 CATHODE EMITTERS

2.4.1 Oxide Cathodes

The typical production-type oxide cathode is a coating of barium and strontium oxides on a base metal such as nickel. The oxide layer is formed by first coating a nickel can or disc with a mixture of barium and strontium carbonates, suspended in a binder material. The mixture is approximately 60 per cent barium carbonate and 40 per cent strontium carbonate. During vacuum processing of the tubes, they are baked out at high temperature. The binder is burned away, and the carbonates are subsequently reduced to oxides. The cathode is now "activated" and will emit electrons. The typical oxide cathode operates CW at about 1000° Kelvin and is capable of roughly 200 to 300 mA per cm^2 at a typical emission efficiency of 200 to 300 mA per watt of heater power. The high emission current capability for each watt of heating power is one of the main advantages of the oxide cathode. Other advantages are high peak emission capability for short pulses and a low operating temperature.

Oxide cathodes are susceptible to deterioration due to ion bombardment; oxide-cathode tubes are usually limited in plate voltage because of this characteristic. Fortunately, high voltage is very seldom needed because of the high currents available at low voltage.

The oxide cathode material will evaporate during the life of the tube, causing free barium to migrate to other areas within the tube. The evaporation can be minimized in the design by means of a high efficiency cathode which runs as cool as possible but still is not emission-limited at the desired heater voltage. In the field, the heater voltage must not exceed the designed value. An oxide cathode which is overheated gives very little more useful emission, but the life of the tube is shortened significantly. Figure 10 is representative of an oxide cathode.

Figure 10. Typical oxide cathode.

2.4.2 Thoriated Tungsten Filaments

A thoriated tungsten filament is one form of an atomic-film emitter. Thorium is added to the tungsten in the process of making tungsten wire. Typically, about 1.5 per cent of thorium in the form of thoria (thorium oxide, ThO_2) is added. By proper processing during vacuum pumping of the tube envelope, the metallic thorium is brought to the surface of the filament wire, and emission increases approximately 1000 times. The thoriated tungsten filament is also carburized. The small amount of tungsten carbide formed in the carburizing process reduces the evaporation rate of the thorium and thus increases the life of the filament. At a typical operating temperature of approximately 1900°K, a thoriated tungsten filament will produce a specific peak emission of about 70 to 100 mA per watt of filament heating power. This is normally

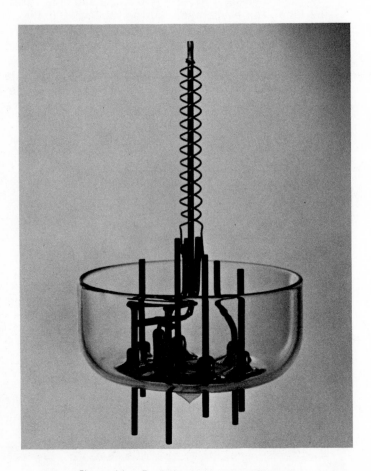

Figure 11. Typical spiral tungsten filament.

5 to 10 mA of CW plate current per watt of filament power. A thoriated tungsten filament is more tolerant of ion bombardment than an oxide cathode, and, therefore, higher voltages can be applied to the tube.

Thoriated tungsten filaments can be assembled in several different configurations. Figures 11, 12 and 13 show typical spiral, bar and mesh filament construction techniques. The spiral filament is used quite extensively in the lower power tubes. As the size of the tube increases, mechanical considerations dictate the bar filament construction technique with spring loading to compensate for thermal expansion. The mesh filament can be used on both small and larger tubes, and is more rugged, therefore, less subject to damage from shock and vibration.

Figure 12.   Typical bar tungsten filament.

Figure 13. Typical mesh tungsten filament.

2.4.3 Gun Type Emitters

Some power grid tubes are designed as a series of electron gun structures arranged in a cylinder around a center line. This type of construction allows large amounts of plate current to flow and be controlled with a minimum amount of grid interception. With reduced grid interception, less power is dissipated in the grid structures. In the case of the control grid, less driving power is required.

SECTION 3
ELECTRICAL DESIGN CONSIDERATIONS

3.1   CLASS OF OPERATION

Most power grid tubes can be operated in any classification, although a few types are not recommended for operation in the positive grid region. This is because the control grid structures are designed for very high gain, and therefore the grid dissipation rating is quite low. The 4CX1000A and the 4CX350A are tubes of this type.

The angle of plate current flow determines the class of operation. Class A is generally considered to be a 360° conduction angle, Class B is 180° conduction angle and Class C is less than 180°. Class AB is in the region between 180° and 360° of conduction angle. The subscript "1" means that no grid current flows. The subscript "2" means that grid current flows.

Example: Class AB_2 operation denotes a plate current conduction angle of 180 to 360 degrees and that grid current is flowing.

The class of operation has nothing to do with whether the amplifier is grid-driven or cathode-driven. A cathode-driven amplifier, for example, can be operated in any desired class. The class of operation is only a function of the plate current conduction angle. The efficiency of an amplifier is also a function of the plate current conduction angle.

The efficiency of conversion of d-c to a-f or r-f power is one of the important characteristics of a vacuum tube. The d-c power which is not converted to useful output power is, for the most part, converted to heat. This heat represents wasted power, and the result of low efficiency is increased operating cost for power. Low efficiency compounds itself. The wasted power must be dissipated, requiring increased blower ratings.

19

Heat exchangers may be needed to cool the equipment. The increased dissipation requires tubes with increased power ratings, and also requires increased ratings on all power supply components. Thus, for a given application, and in all but the very lowest power applications, the efficiency must be carefully considered, consistent with the other requirements of the system. Figure 14 presents the theoretical efficiency attainable with a tuned, or resistive, load assuming peak a-c plate voltage is equal to plate supply voltage.

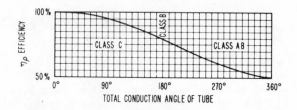

Figure 14. Plate efficiency vs. conduction angle for an amplifier with tuned load.
(From Thomas L. Martin, Jr., "Electronic Circuits," p. 452, Prentice-Hall, Inc., Englewood Cliffs, N.J., 1955).

A Class A power amplifier is used in applications requiring large amounts of low harmonic distortion power output. A Class A amplifier can be operated with very low intermodulation distortion in linear r-f amplifier service (see Section 4). Typical plate efficiency for a Class A amplifier is about 30 percent. The power gain is quite high due to the very low drive power required. Gains as high as 30 db are typical. Class A service is widely used in audio amplifier service and regulator service.

A Class AB power amplifier is capable of generating more power, with the same tube, than the Class A amplifier, but more intermodulation distortion is generated at the same time. A Class B r-f linear amplifier will generate still more intermodulation distortion, but is acceptable in certain applications. The plate efficiency is typically 66 percent, and stage gain is about 20 to 25 db. Class B is used widely in audio amplifier applications, such as modulators for high level amplitude modulation.

A Class C power amplifier is used where large amounts of r-f power are to be generated with high efficiency. A Class C amplifier operates much like a limiter; therefore, it cannot amplify a modulated driver without serious distortion. Class C amplifiers are used for high level amplitude modulation wherein the plate voltage, or plate and screen voltage for tetrodes, is varied at an audio rate. Class C amplifiers must be used with tuned circuits or with a commutating output circuit with filtering. Class C cannot be used in the normal audio amplifier circuit.

3.2   TUBE PERFORMANCE COMPUTER FOR R-F AMPLIFIERS

It is quite easy to make a close estimate of the performance of a vacuum tube in radio-frequency power amplifier service, or an approximation in the case of harmonic amplifier service. Such estimates will give r-f output power, d-c input power, grid driving power, and all d-c current values.

> These estimates can be easily made by using the EIMAC Tube Performance Computer.   This can be obtained at no cost by writing to: Application Engineering Department, Varian, EIMAC Division, 301 Industrial Way, San Carlos, CA 94070 USA. The computer is used with the characteristic curves of the tube, as plotted on plate voltage/grid voltage coordinates   (constant current curves).

By graphically laying out the trace of the plate and grid voltages as they rise and fall about the applied d-c plate voltage and d-c grid bias, a clear understanding of the action taking place within a tube is possible. With such an understanding, the operating conditions can be readily altered to suit individual requirements.

3.2.1   Simple Action in Class C R-F Amplifiers

In an amplifier a varying voltage is applied to the control grid of the tube. Simultaneously the plate voltage will vary in a similar manner, due to the action of the amplified current flowing in the plate circuit. In radio-frequency applications with resonant circuits, these voltage variations are smooth sine-wave variations, 180° out of phase (as the grid voltage rises and becomes **more** positive, the plate voltage falls and becomes **less** positive), as indicated in Figure 15. Note how these variations center about the d-c plate voltage and the d-c control grid bias.

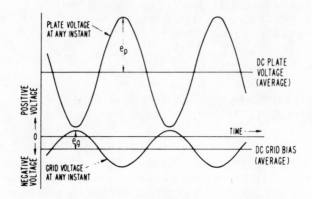

Figure 15.   Variation of plate and grid voltage

Now let us see how such variations of the plate and grid voltages of a tube appear on the constant-current curves of a tube. In Figure 16 these variations have been indicated next to the plate voltage and grid voltage scales of a typical constant current curve. At some instant of time, shown as "t" on the time scales, the grid voltage has a value which is the point marked "eg" on the grid-voltage sine wave. If one finds the point on the tube curves corresponding to these

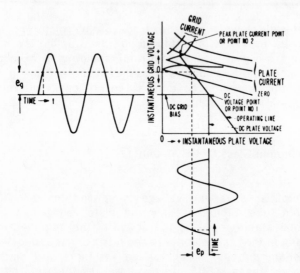

Figure 16.   Plate voltage and grid voltage scales

values (where a line drawn from "e_g" and a line drawn from "e_p" cross) he will be at Point A in Figure 16. As the values of the grid voltage "e_g" and plate voltage "e_p" vary over the r-f cycle, Point A moves up and down a line, which in the case of the normal r-f power amplifier is a straight line. This line is called the "Operating Line."

Any point on the operating line (when drawn on constant-current curves as illustrated in Figures 16 or 18) tells the instantaneous values of plate current, screen current, and grid current which must flow when these particular values of grid and plate voltage are applied to the tube. Thus, by reading off the values of the currents and plotting them against time "t", one can obtain a curve of instantaneous values of plate and grid current (Figure 17).

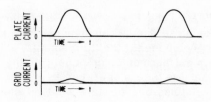

Figure 17. Instantaneous values of plate and grid current.

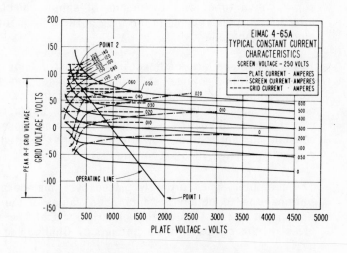

Figure 18. Constant current characteristics for 4-65A tetrode

23

If we analyze the plate and grid-current values shown, we can predict that they will cause a d-c ammeter to show a particular reading. This is called the d-c component of the current. Also, we can predict that if the plate current flows through a properly-loaded resonant r-f circuit, a certain amount of radio-frequency power will be delivered to that circuit. If the circuit is tuned to the fundamental frequency (same frequency as the r-f grid voltage) the power delivered will be due to the fundamental, or principal, radio-frequency component of plate current. If the circuit is tuned to a harmonic of the grid-voltage frequency, e.g., two or three times the frequency, the power delivered will be due to a harmonic component of the plate current.

3.2.2   Use of the EIMAC Tube Performance Computer

The EIMAC Tube Performance Computer provides the means to make these simple calculations. It is a means to determine the d-c component, the fundamental r-f component, or the approximate harmonic component of the current flowing in a tube when the tube is operating as a radio-frequency amplifier. It also enables one to state what all meter readings will be, and to predict the r-f output power and the required driving power. With these factors known, we are able to forecast what will happen if any of the operating conditions are changed.

The EIMAC Tube Performance Computer is a simple aid to enable the selection of suitable values from the characteristic curves of a tube, and by means of simple calculations to forecast the performance of the tube in radio-frequency power amplifier applications.

The basic steps are outlined under "Instructions" on the computer. This requires selecting d-c plate and grid-bias voltages, being guided by the typical operating values given on the technical data sheet for the tube type under investigation. Next, a suitable "operating line" must be chosen on the constant-current curves for the tube type (plotted on the grid-voltage/plate-voltage coordinates).

The computer, when properly placed over this operating line, permits one to obtain instantaneous values of the currents flowing at every 15° of the electrical cycle. The formulas given on the computer were derived by Chaffee [1] to give the

---

1 E. L. Chaffee,"A Simplified Harmonic Analysis," Review Sci. Inst. 7, October 1936, p. 384.

various average and harmonic components of the resulting currents. Knowing these current component values and the radio-frequency voltage values which are indicated through use of the computer, one can readily calculate the complete performance of the tube.

The fundamental methods of making such computations, the considerations necessary to stay within the ratings of the tube types while accomplishing various forms of modulation have been covered in literature.[2,3,4,5,6] The method for the case of harmonic amplifier service is approximate and should be used only for tetrode and pentode tubes where the plate voltage has little effect on the amount of plate current flowing. A more exact method, showing that for harmonic operating the operating line is a simple Lissajou figure, has been described by Brown.

The results obtained by using this computer for power-amplifier service can be applied in combination with the other methods given in the literature to give good accuracy with simplified procedures. The resulting accuracy is well within the normal variation of tube characteristics due to the normal variation in manufacturing dimensions of a tube. Since the published curves are only typical of the characteristics to be expected of a particular tube type, the calculated performance will be well within the values obtained when different tubes of a given tube type are operated under the assumed conditions.

3.2.3 Example Showing Detailed Use of the Computer in Class C R-F Power Amplifiers

Assume that we have an EIMAC 4-65A tetrode and want to make it work efficiently. Also assume that we have a 2000 volt d-c power supply available.

2 H. P. Thomas, "Determination of Grid Driving Power in Radio Frequency Power Amplifiers," Proc. IRE, Vol. 21, Aug. 1933, pp. 1134-1141.

3 W. G. Wagener, "Simplified Methods for Computing Performance of Transmitting Tubes," Proc. IRE, January 1937.

4 R. I. Sarbacher, "Graphical Determination of PA Performance," Electronics, December 1942.

5 R. I. Sarbacher, "Performance of Self Biased Modulated Amplifier," Electronics, April 1943.

6 Robert H. Brown, "Harmonic Amplifier Design,"Proc. IRE, Vol. 35, August 1947, pp. 771-777.

Within frequency limits, we know that a tube should be able to run in Class C amplifier service with about 75% efficiency, or in other words, to convert 75% of the d-c plate input power to r-f output power. The difference, or 25% of the input power, is dissipated and lost as heat on the plate of the tube. The d-c plate input power is then about four times the power dissipated on the plate.

The 4-65A tetrode has a maximum rated plate dissipation of 65 watts. To illustrate performance near the maximum rating, we will choose an input power about four times the dissipation rating, or about 260 watts per tube. At 2000 volts the plate current per tube must then be 130 mA. It is usual practice in the case of tetrodes and medium or low μ triodes in Class C amplifier service for the d-c grid bias voltage to be roughly two or three times the grid voltage necessary to cut off the flow of plate current. By referring to the curves for the 4-65A, we decide to use a d-c grid bias voltage of -130 volts.

Let us now locate the "operating line" on the constant-current curves for the 4-65A. (See Figure 18.) First, mark the point where the d-c grid bias and d-c plate voltage cross. The "operating line" must go through this point, which can be referred to as "Point No. 1." Next, we must decide what the peak value of plate current must be and how low we can let the instantaneous value of plate voltage go when the tube is passing this much current. This is necessary in order to locate the other end of the "operating line," e.g., "Point No. 2."

The peak value of plate current in Class C amplifiers usually runs about four times the d-c plate current. The minimum value of instantaneous plate voltage is usually set by the fact that if the voltage is too low, the grid current in triodes and the screen current in tetrodes will be needlessly high, resulting in high grid or screen dissipation. Little will be gained as far as output power is concerned. The minimum value of plate voltage is usually in the region where the plate constant-current curves bend upward. (See Figure 18.) In the case of triodes, this is near the "diode line," where the instantaneous plate and grid voltages are equal. The practical procedure in calculating tube performance is to arbitrarily choose Point No. 2, complete the calculations, and compare the results.

In the case of the 4-65A, let us choose a peak value of plate current about four times that of the d-c plate current of 130 mA, or 500 mA. Let us choose a minimum instantaneous plate voltage of 250 volts, and thus fix the upper end of the

26

"operating line." Locate this point on the tube curves, and refer to it as Point No. 2 in Figure 18. (The plate currents which flow at various combinations of plate and grid voltages are shown by the plate-current lines.) The value of current for each line is noted. In-between values can be estimated closely enough for our purposes. Draw a straight line between Points 1 and 2. This line is the "operating line," and shows the current and voltage values at each instant in the r-f cycle when the current is being taken from the tube. The non-conducting half of the r-f cycle would be shown by extending the line an equal distance on the opposite side of Point No. 1. There is little to be gained by this line extension, since no current flows during this half of the cycle.

The EIMAC Tube Performance Computer can now be used to obtain the meter readings and power values from this "operating line." Place the computer on the constant-current curve so that the "guide lines" of the computer are parallel with the operating line. Slide the computer (without turning it) until the line OG passes through the d-c voltage point No. 1, and line OA passes through the peak-current Point No. 2. Be sure the guide lines are still parallel to the **"operating line."**

Note that the lines OB, OC, OD, OE, and OF all cross over the operating line.

At each point where the lines OA, OB, etc. cross the "operating line," we must determine the instantaneous values of plate current and grid current (and screen current if a tetrode or pentode is used) which are flowing at that particular moment in the r-f cycle. Later, from these key values of current, values of plate current, grid current, screen current, and the r-f components of the plate current may be calculated.

These current values should be listed for each point where the lines OA, OB, etc. cross the operating line so that they can be combined later to calculate the various tube currents. At points where OE and OF cross, the current values are usually zero for Class C operation.

In the examples chosen, read off the instantaneous plate-current values where these lines cross the "operating line." At the point where the line OA crosses the operating line, the plate current is 500 mA. Where OB crosses the operating line, the plate current is also 500 mA. At OC the plate current is about 450 mA, OD is 300 mA, OE is 90 mA, and OF and OG are 0 mA. Similarly, the instantaneous screen current at the crossing of OA and the operating line is 200 mA, and the instantaneous grid current is almost 80 mA. Values are

27

read for the other crossover points and written down. These values are put into columns for calculation:

Crossing of line	Simplified name in Formulas	Instantaneous values of currents		
		Plate	Screen	Control grid
OA	A	500 mA	200 mA	80 mA
OB	B	500	155	70
OC	C	450	60	42
OD	D	300	15	17
OE	E	90	0	0
OF	F	0	0	0

In order to obtain the d-c value of plate, screen, and control grid currents the formula (see computer) indicated that the above values should be added, using only one-half the A values (giving 250 mA for plate, 100 mA for screen, and 40 mA for grid), and then divided by 12, as follows:

D-C meter reading = $1/12 \, (0.5A + B + C + D + E + F)$

Plate	Screen	Control Grid
250 mA	100 mA	40 mA
500	155	70
450	60	42
300	15	17
90	0	0
0	0	0

Total 1590 mA   330 mA   169 mA

D-C current = 1/12 total = (approximately)
133 mA   28 mA   14 mA

To calculate the r-f output power it is necessary to use the formula for the peak r-f current, which is present in the tube plate current. Since the tube is being used as a straight r-f power amplifier, use the formula for "Peak Fundamental R-F" as shown on the computer. If estimating the performance of a doubler or tripler, use the formula for "Peak 2nd Harmonic R-F" or "Peak 3rd Harmonic R-F."

From the computer, it may be seen that the formula for the peak fundamental r-f current is:

$1/12 \, (A + 1.93B + 1.73C + 1.41D + E + 0.52F)$

A =	500	= 500 mA
1.93B =	1.93 x 500	= 965
1.73C =	1.73 x 450	= 778
1.41D =	1.41 x 300	= 423
E =	90	= 90

Total   = 2756 mA

Peak fundamental current = 1/12 total
= 2756/12 = 230 mA

The various current values are now at hand. In order to calculate the powers involved, it is necessary to know not only the d-c voltage values but the greatest amount each value swings away from the d-c value. This is known as the peak value of the r-f voltage. Because the plate voltage swings from 2000 volts down to 250 volts, the peak r-f plate voltage is the difference between these two figures, or 1750 volts. Similarly, the grid voltage must rise and fall between the operating points No. 1 and No. 2, or from -130 volts to +90 volts. This is a peak swing of 220 volts, and the peak r-f grid voltage is 220 volts.

Now use the formula for output power and driving power: Output power = one-half r-f plate current x peak r-f plate voltage.

The peak r-f plate current is found to be 230 mA (or .230 ampere), and the peak r-f plate voltage is found to be 1750 volts.

So: Output Power	1 2 x 0.230 x 1750 = 201 watts.
and Input Power	= d c Plate Current x d c Plate Voltage 0.133 x 2000 = 266 watts
Plate Dissipation	d c Input Power - r f Output Power 266 - 201 = 65 watts
Efficiency	= r f Output Power divided by d c Input Power = 201 266 = 75.5%
Driving Power	= d c Grid Current x Peak R-F Grid Voltage = 0.014 x 220 = 3.1 watts

The power consumed by the bias source is the product of the d-c grid current and the d-c grid voltage, or 0.014 x 130 = 1.7 watts.

The difference between the driving power and the power consumed by the bias source is the power dissipated on the control grid, or 3.1 - 1.7 = 1.4 watts.

The power dissipated on the screen grid is the product of the d-c screen current and the d-c screen voltage, because the screen grid has no impedance between it and the d-c screen supply. Thus it is 0.028 x 250 = 7.0 watts.

The performance of the tube can be summarized:

d c Plate Voltage	2000 volts	Driving Power	3.1 watts
d c Screen Voltage	250 volts	Grid Dissipation	1.4 watts
d c Grid Voltage	-130 volts	Screen Dissipation	7.0 watts
d c Plate Current	133 mA	Plate Input Power	266 watts
d c Screen Current	28 mA	Plate Output Power	201 watts
Peak r f Grid Voltage	220 volts	Plate Dissipation	65 watts

3.2.4 Use of EIMAC Tube Performance Computer for Class A, AB, and B Service

While the EIMAC Tube Performance Computer is primarily designed for use in Class C service, it may be used for Class A, AB, and B service where the idling (quiescent) plate current is not zero. To calculate performance for operating conditions having a large order of idling plate current, the plate current flow during the positive half of the plate voltage swing becomes appreciable and cannot be ignored. When the tube functions over 180 degrees or more of the operating cycle, a full set of ordinate points must be employed for the computations. The computer is therefore used in a two-step process.

First, determine the operating line. The computer is used in the normal fashion to derive the instantaneous values of plate, screen, and grid current during the negative half of the plate voltage swing. These current points are logged as explained under the Class C service description.

Now, determine the instantaneous current points over the positive portion of the plate voltage cycle. Combine these with the points taken for the negative half of the cycle. This is done in the following fashion: a line is penciled on the computer over the operating line, and of equivalent length. The computer is now **inverted and rotated 180°** and again aligned with the chosen operating line on the constant current curve, so that **inverted** point G falls on the idling current value (Point No. 1) and inverted **point A** passes through a minimum peak current point representing maximum positive plate voltage swing. The penciled line on the computer now represents an extension of the operating line into the area of positive peak voltage swing. The extended operating line is a straight line, twice as long as the original operating line. Instantaneous values of plate, screen, and grid current (if any) are those observed where the reversed ordinate lines on the computer cross the extended operating line.

The current points measured with the computer **inverted** are logged and these, together with the points obtained in the first operation (computer right side up) provide a full set of instantaneous peak current values necessary for the calculation of Class A, AB, or B parameters. With the first set of computer readings termed A, B, C, D, E, F and G, the second (inverted) set of figures may be termed A', B', C', D', E', and F', with the sets used in the following formulae, which are modifications of Chaffee's permitting the use of current values directly from the constant current curves:

(1) D. C. Current (Meter Reading) $= \frac{1}{12} \left[\frac{A + A'}{2} + (B + B') + (C + C') + (D + D') + (E + E') + (F + F') + G \right]$

(2) Peak Fundamental RF Current $= \frac{1}{12} [(A - A') + 1.93 (B - B') + 1.73 (C - C') + 1.41 (D - D') + (E - E') + 0.52 (F - F')]$

(3) Approx 2d Harmonic RF current (tetrodes or pentodes only) $= \frac{1}{12} [(A + A') + 1.73 (B + B') + (C + C') - (E + E') - 1.73 (F + F') - 2G]$

(4) Approx. 3d Harmonic RF current (tetrodes or pentodes only) $= \frac{1}{12} [(A - A') + 1.41 (B - B') - 1.41 (D - D') - 2(E - E') - 1.41 (F - F')]$

(5) Power Output $= \frac{\text{Peak Fundamental RF current x Peak RF voltage}}{2}$

(6) Resonant Load Impedance $= \frac{\text{Peak RF Voltage}}{\text{Peak Fund. RF Current}}$

3.2.5 An Example: Using the Computer for Class AB$_1$ Service

Operating data is to be derived for an EIMAC 4CW100,000D tetrode operating at a plate potential of 10 kV with a screen potential of 1.5 kV. Assume that power output design goal for this particular application is about 60kW. Grid current is zero; that is, the tube is operated in the Class AB$_1$ mode, with the grid never being driven positive.

Within frequency limits, a plate circuit efficiency of about 55-60% may be assumed for Class AB$_1$ operation. Maximum d-c plate input is therefore 2.2 to 2.75 times the anode dissipation. A maximum power input of 2.2 x 50,000 = 110 kW is chosen. At 10kV, the maximum d-c plate current is then 11.0 A. This is within the maximum rated plate current of 15 A for Class AB$_1$ service as specified on the data sheet.

For Class AB service the tube does not operate in a cut-off condition, but rather a certain value of idling plate current exists. This must be taken into account when choosing Point 1 on the constant current curve. Generally speaking, high levels of resting plate current provide reduced levels of intermodulation distortion products and somewhat lower plate efficiency. Idling plate current is usually chosen so that anode dissipation under quiescent conditions is about 50-70% of the maximum dissipation rating. In the following example, idling plate current is chosen to be 4.5 amperes. From Figure 19, it may be determined that a grid potential of about -295 volts is required to produce the desired plate current at the chosen screen and plate potentials. The intersection of the -295 volt bias line and the 10 kV plate line determines the idling point on the operating line (Point No. 1).

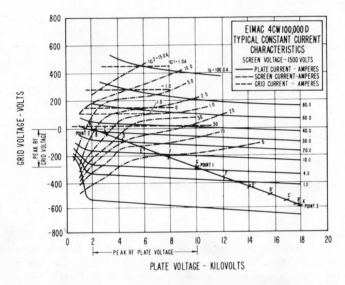

Figure 19. Constant current characteristics for 4CW100,000D tetrode.

Next, the peak value of plate current must be determined, and the minimum amount of instantaneous plate voltage chosen to pass this amount of current. Determination of these values will locate Point No. 2 and will thus define the operating line.

Class AB_1 service limits grid voltage excursions to negative grid regions on the constant current graph. Point No. 2 therefore may never be located above the zero grid voltage line. In addition, the minimum instantaneous plate voltage is usually not allowed to swing as low as the d-c screen potential, since screen dissipation tends to become abnormally high. The location of Point No. 2 thus has certain restrictive limits defined by screen dissipation and the maximum positive grid signal voltage. In this case, for the 4CW100,000D, minimum instantaneous place voltage is about 2 kV. Peak r-f voltage is thus $10,000 - 2,000 = 8,000$ volts.

Peak r-f plate current in a Class AB$_1$ amplifier usually runs about 2.5 to 3.0 times the average d-c plate current. In this case, a maximum peak plate current of about 2.9 times the maximum signal d-c plate current of 11.0 A, or 32 amperes, is chosen. This defines Point No. 2, which is at the intersection of the 2 kV minimum plate voltage line and thus falls within the limits discussed in the preceding paragraph. A straight line is drawn between Point No. 1 and Point No. 2 which is the negative plate cycle portion of the operating line.

When the operating line is extended to the right of Point No. 1, it can be observed that the tube conducts over the rest of the cycle where (by virtue of the "flywheel" effect of the resonant tank circuit) the instantaneous plate voltage swings as far above the normal d-c value as it swings below. It is important to note that operation with less than cutoff bias requires that the EIMAC Tube Performance Computer employ points on the operating line falling to the right of Point No. 1. The operating line is accordingly extended and the computer is used in a two-part operation, as shown in the following example:

4CW100,000D COMPUTATIONS

d-c Plate Voltage = 10 kV	Power Input	=	110 kW
d-c Screen Voltage =1.5 kV	Max. d-c Plate Current	=	11 amp.
	Zero-Signal Plate Current =		4.5 amp.
	d-c Grid Voltage	=	-295 volts
Constant Current Graph and	Peak Plate Current	=	32 amp.
Operating Line determine:	Peak RF Voltage	=	8,000

Step One			Step Two		
EIMAC Computer Readings			Inverted Computer Readings		
Instantaneous Peak Current (amps)			Instantaneous Peak Current (amps)		
Ordinate Crossing	Plate	Screen	Ordinate Crossing	Plate	Screen
A	32	3	A'	0.20	—
B	31	2	B'	0.25	—
C	28	1.2	C'	0.30	—
D	22	0.25	D'	0.50	—
E	15	0.07	E'	0.80	—
F	9	—	F'	1.50	—
G	4.5	—			

d-c Plate Current	$= \frac{1}{12}\left[\frac{32.2}{2} + 31.25 + 28.3 + 22.5 + 15.8 + 10.5 + 4.5\right] = 10.75$ amp.
Plate Power Input	$= 10$ KV x 10.75A $= 107,500$ watts
Peak Fundamental RF Current	$= \frac{1}{12}$ [31.8 + 59.4 + 47.7 + 30.3 + 14.2 + 3.9] $= 15.6$ amp.
Power Output	$= \frac{15.6 \times 8000}{2} = 62,500$ watts
Plate Dissipation	$= 45,000$ watts
Efficiency	$= \frac{62,500}{107,500} \times 100 = 58.2\%$
Resonant Load Impedance	$= \frac{8000}{15.6} = 512$ ohms
d-c Screen Current	$= \frac{1}{12}\left[\frac{3}{2} + 2 + 1.2 + 0.25 + 0.07\right] = 417$ mA.

3.3 TYPICAL R-F AMPLIFIER CIRCUIT DESIGNS

In the previous discussion of tube performance calculations, an example was worked out using the 4-65A in Class C r-f service. Using the obtained operating parameters, it is now possible to demonstrate the next step in the circuit design. For the benefit of discussion, it will be assumed the desired output circuit is a shunt-fed pi-network; it will also be assumed that the grid circuit is to be tuned by a conventional parallel tuned circuit. The circuit will be as shown in Figure 20.

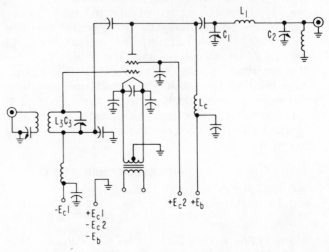

Figure 20. A typical circuit for an R-F amplifier.

The first step in designing the output circuit is to specify the resonant load impedance of the tube, the loaded Q of the circuit and the desired output impedance of the network. The resonant plate load impedance for the 4-65A is determined by dividing the plate peak r-f voltage swing by the plate peak fundamental r-f current.

$$\text{Resonant Load Impedance} = \frac{\text{Peak r-f Voltage}}{\text{Peak Fundamental r-f Current}}$$

$$R_L = \frac{1750 \text{ volts}}{.230 \text{ amps}} = 7600 \text{ ohms}$$

If it is assumed that the output impedance of the network is to be 50 ohms, and the loaded Q is to be 15, the output tuned circuit may now be designed. The output impedance of 50 ohms will match into a properly terminated 50 ohm transmission line. The loaded Q of 15 is a compromise between circuit efficiency and harmonic attenuation (see Figure 21). Figures 22, 23 and 24 are design graphs for matching typical

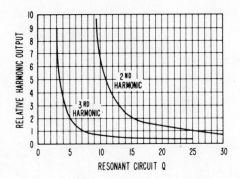

Figure 21. Relative harmonic output vs. resonant circuit Q.

A resonant circuit with a loaded Q of 10 to 20 is usually considered optimum. A lower loaded Q will result in greater harmonic output. A higher loaded Q will result in higher circulating current with increased loss
in the coil. The loaded Q is determined by the L/C ratio and the load resistance.

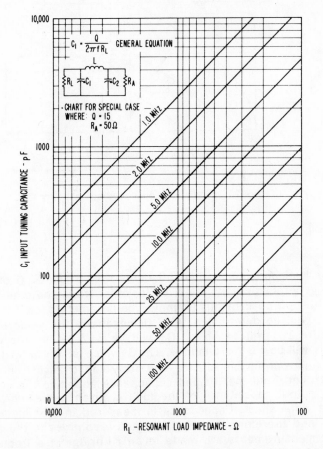

Figure 22. Determination of input capacitor C_1.

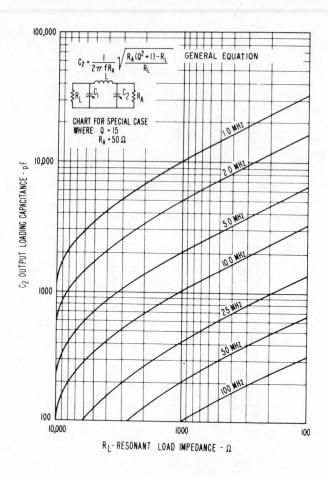

Figure 23. Determination of loading capacitor C_2.

tube load impedances into 50 ohms with a loaded Q of 15. The general equations are given for other loads and other Q's. For the purpose of this example, the parameters for 7 megahertz will be determined. At 7.0 megahertz the value of C_1 (Figure 22) will be 45 pf, C_2 will be 317 pf and the value of L_1 will be 11 microhenries. The C_1 value of 45 pF includes the tube output capacitance, the stray capacitance from tube to ground, and the lumped capacitance added to the circuit. The output capacitance of the tube is given in the individual tube data sheet. Capacitance is measured in a shielded fixture and therefore the value obtained is confined to the tube. The measurements are made in an r-f bridge at a frequency of 100 to 465 kilohertz.

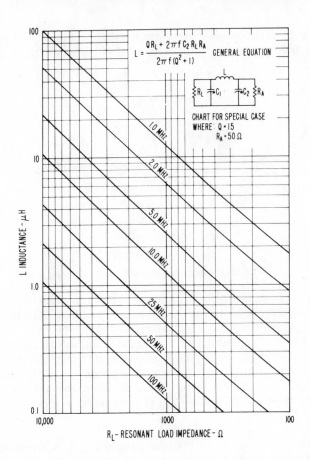

Figure 24A. Determination of inductor L.

The inductance of the plate choke, L_C, in Figure 20 may be determined by noting that it is in shunt with the tuned circuit. If the r-f current through the choke is to be limited to one per cent of the tuned circuit circulating current, the inductance of L_C must be 100 times that of coil L. The inductance of L_C would then be 1.2 millihenries. The series resonant frequency of the choke must be determined to be outside of the operating range of the amplifier. This can be checked by shorting the ends of the choke together with a low inductance strap and measuring the series resonant frequency by means of a grid-dip meter.

It is also important to determine the parallel resonant frequency of the choke due to its stray capacitance. The choke will exhibit inductive reactance below the parallel resonant frequency and capacitive reactance above the parallel resonant

37

frequency. The parallel resonant frequency must therefore be above the operating frequency of the amplifier by a small amount.

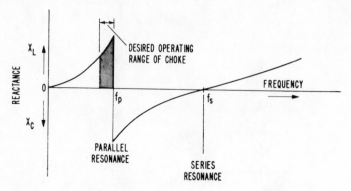

Figure 24B. Reactance of an r-f choke vs. frequency.

The design of a typical grid tuned circuit is quite similar to the design of the plate resonant circuit. For Class C operation, or any class where there is grid current flow, the input circuit must have sufficient Q to maintain a sinusoidal grid waveshape. The input resistance loads the grid tuned circuit. It is generally considered good engineering practice to have a Q of between 12 and 15. In any class of operation with no grid current flowing, the grid circuit requirements are not as stringent.

For the 4-65A example, the input resistance is approximately the power delivered to the grid of the tube divided by the square of the d-c grid current.

$$R = \frac{P}{I^2}$$

R = input resistance
P = power delivered to grid
I = d-c grid current

$$R = \frac{1.4 \text{ watts}}{(.014 \text{ amps})^2} = 7140 \text{ ohms}$$

$$X_c = X_L = \frac{R}{Q}$$

X_c = capacitive reactance of input circuit
X_L = inductive reactance of input circuit
Q = loaded Q of grid circuit

$$X_c = X_L = \frac{7140}{15} = 476 \text{ ohms}$$

The input circuit capacitance, C_3, for 7 megahertz operation will, therefore, be 48 pF. The input circuit inductance, L_3, will be about 10 microhenries.

A further point of interest is the magnitude of the current necessary to charge the input and output capacitances of a vacuum tube. These capacitances must be charged and discharged during each cycle. The input capacitance of the 4-65A is 6.0 to 8.3 pF. Output capacitance is 1.9 to 2.6 pF. For this discussion, it will be assumed the input capacitance is 7 pF, and the output capacitance is 2 pF. With these values of capacitance, the input capacitive reactance at 7 megahertz is 3400 ohms and the output reactance is about 12,000 ohms. In the 4-65A example the grid voltage swing is 220 volts. Therefore, the grid peak charging current will be 220/340 or 0.647 amperes. The peak plate voltage swing is 1750 volts. Therefore, the plate peak charging current will be 1750/12,000 or 0.146 amperes. Current values are quite low in this case, because the frequency of operation and the tube capacitances are low. If the 4-65A is operated under the same conditions at ten times the frequency (70 MHz), the charging currents will be ten times the 7 MHz example. The greater the charging currents the greater the tube seal heating, electrode heating, circuit losses, and the greater the current in the screen by-pass capacitor. At the higher frequencies, it is sometimes better to limit the plate voltage swing and raise the plate current. This technique reduces the magnitude of the plate circuit charging current.

3.4   COMPONENT PARTS

If one is to maintain the isolation of the output and input circuits, some thought must be given to the location of the component parts of the amplifier. All component parts of the grid or input circuit and any earlier stages must be kept out of the plate circuit compartment. Similarly, plate circuit parts must be kept out of the input compartment. It must be noted, however, that in the case of the tetrode and pentode the screen lead of the tube and connections via the socket are common to both the output and input resonant circuits. Due to the plate to screen capacitance of a tetrode or pentode, the r-f plate voltage (developed in the output circuit) causes an r-f current to flow out the screen lead to the chassis. In the case of a push-pull stage, this current may flow from the screen terminal of one tube to the screen terminal of the other tube. Similarly, due to the grid-to-screen capacitance of the tube, the r-f voltage in the input circuit will cause an r-f current to flow in this same screen lead to the chassis, or to the opposite tube of the push-pull circuit.

The inductance of the lead common to both the output and input circuits has the desirable feature of providing voltage of opposite polarity to neutralize the feedback voltage of the residual plate to control grid capacitance of the tube (this is discussed under "Neutralization," Section 5). It should be noted, however, that the mutual coupling from the screen lead to the input resonant circuit may be a possible source of trouble if accentuated.

In the case of the grounded-grid triode the control grid and associated leads are common to the output and input circuits. The inductance of the control grid lead can help or hinder the stabilization of a grounded-grid amplifier (this is discussed under "Neutralization," Section 5).

3.5 LEAD LENGTHS

Some of the interconnecting lead wires close to the tube should be designed with extremely low inductance to minimize the chances of forming possible VHF parasitic circuits. If two or more tubes are used they should be placed reasonably close together to help provide short interconnecting leads. The lead lengths of radio frequency circuits involving the fundamental frequency can usually be much longer; the length will depend a good deal upon the frequency of the fundamental. All of the d-c, keying, modulating, and control circuit wires can be quite long if properly filtered and arranged away from the active r-f circuits.

The following interconnecting lead wires in a tetrode or pentode power amplifier should preferably have quite low inductance: filament and screen by-pass leads, suppressor by-pass leads, leads from the grid and the plate to the tuning capacitor of the r-f circuit and return, and the interconnections from tube to tube in push-pull or parallel arrangements (except for parasitic suppressors in the plate). For a lead to have low inductance, it must have a large surface and be short in length, as in a strap or a ribbon. This consideration also applies to that portion of a lead inside a by-pass capacitor.

3.6 FILAMENT BY-PASSING

Low inductance by-pass capacitors should be used in by-passing the filament. It is good practice to place a capacitor directly between the filament socket terminals. If the circuit allows it, strap one filament directly to the chassis, and if not, use a second by-pass capacitor from one terminal to the chassis.

If two or more tubes are in a push-pull or parallel circuit, one can use a short strap interconnecting one of the filament terminals of each socket. The mid-point of the interconnecting strap can be by-passed or grounded directly.

With tubes having a completely isolating screen cone terminal, the general circuit arrangment is usually different. The filament or cathode should go directly or through by-passes to the cavity wall or chassis to which the screen terminal is by-passed.

3.7 SCREEN AND SUPPRESSOR GRID BY-PASSING AND SCREEN TUNING

Low inductance leads are generally advisable for screen and suppressor grid terminal connections. For all frequencies, it is good practice to route the screen and suppressor by-pass capacitors directly from the screen to one filament terminal. The suppressor grid is by-passed in the same manner when the suppressor is operated with a potential other than cathode potential. With the suppressor operating at cathode potential, the suppressor should be grounded to the chassis directly in a circuit where the cathode is at chassis potential. This applies to tubes in push-pull as well as single tubes. In the VHF region, the connection to the screen terminals, for those tubes with two screen pins, should be made to the mid-point of a strap placed between the two screen terminals of the socket. This provides for equal division of the r-f currents in the screen leads and minimizes the heating effects.

Above the self-neutralizing frequency (see "Neutralization," Section 5) of the tetrode or pentode, the screen by-pass capacitors are sometimes variable. By proper adjustment of this variable capacitor, the amount and phase of the screen r-f voltage can be made to cancel the effects of the feedback capacitance within the tubes. Thus, neutralization is accomplished. The screen lead inductance and the variable capacitor are **not** series resonant. The variable capacitor is adjusted so that a net inductive reactance remains to provide the proper voltage and phase for neutralization.

The preceding paragraphs apply directly to tubes having the screen and suppressor grids mounted on internal supporting lead rods.

The tube types having isolating screen cone terminals seem to work best when the screen or suppressor by-pass capacitor is a flat sandwich type capacitor built directly on to the peripheral screen contacting collet of the socket. The size of the by-pass is a function of the operating frequency. The dielectric material can be Teflon, Mica, Isomica or similar materials.

3.8   GROUNDED-GRID CIRCUITS

The zero-bias triodes, such as the 3-400Z and 3-1000Z, generally are used in grounded grid circuits. The control grid is operated at r-f ground and therefore is similar to the screen grid in a tetrode or pentode. The control grid may be by-passed directly at the socket or operated at d-c ground. The d-c grounded approach is favored because no by-pass capacitors are required. Figures 25 and 26 illustrate the two circuit configurations.

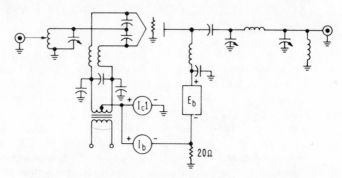

Figure 25. A typical circuit using "zero-bias" triodes showing metering circuits and method of grounding the grid to r-f. The grid current is measured in the return lead from ground to filament.

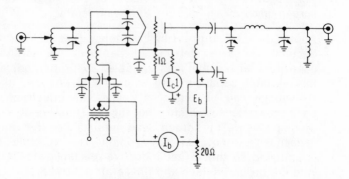

Figure 26. A typical circuit using "zero-bias" triodes showing metering circuits. The grid is grounded to r-f with a by-pass capacitor. The grid is raised 1Ω above d-c ground to allow the grid current to be measured.

3.9   PROTECTION

EIMAC Power Grid Tubes are designed to stand considerable abuse. For instance, the excess anode dissipation resulting from detuning the plate circuit of the tube will have no ill effects if not applied for periods of time sufficient to overheat the envelope and the seal structure.

Similarly, the control, screen and suppressor grids will stand some excess dissipation. The maximum dissipation for each grid indicated on the data sheet should not be exceeded except for time intervals of less than one second. The maximum dissipation rating for each grid structure is usually considerably above typical values used for maximum output so that ample operating leeway is provided. The time of duration of overloads on a grid structure is necessarily short because of the small heat storage capacity of the wires. Furthermore, grid temperatures cannot be seen, so no visual warning of accidental overload is apparent.

The type and degree of protection required in an r-f amplifier against circuit failure will vary with the type of screen and grid voltage supply. Figure 27 is a chart of tetrode and pentode protection as related to certain kinds of circuit failures.

CIRCUIT FAILURE	FIXED SCREEN SUPPLY		SCREEN VOLTAGE THROUGH DROPPING RESISTOR	
	FIXED GRID BIAS	RESISTOR GRID BIAS	FIXED GRID BIAS	RESISTOR GRID BIAS
Loss of Excitation	No Protection Required	Plate Current Relay	Plate Current Relay	Plate Current Relay or Screen Control Circuit
Loss of Antenna Loading	Screen Current Relay	Screen Current Relay	Grid Current Relay	Nothing Required
Excess Antenna Loading	Screen Under-Current Relay	Screen Under-Current Relay	Plate Current Relay	Plate Current Relay
Failure of Plate Supply	Screen Current Relay	Screen Current Relay	Grid Current Relay	Nothing Required
Failure of Screen Supply	Grid Current Relay	Nothing Required	—	—
Failure of Grid Bias Supply	Plate Current Relay or Screen Current Relay	—	Plate Current Relay Grid Current Relay	—

Figure 27. Tetrode and pentode protection chart.

This chart indicates the location of a suitable relay which should act to remove the principal supply voltage from the stage or transmitter to prevent damage to the tubes.

For screen voltage taken through a dropping resistor from the plate supply, a plate relay provides almost universal protection. For a fixed screen supply a relay provides protection in most cases. For protection against excess antenna loading and consequent high plate dissipation, a screen undercurrent relay may also be used in some services.

The plate, screen and bias voltages may be applied simultaneously to a tetrode. The same holds true for a pentode, plus the application of the suppressor voltage. In a grid driven amplifier, the grid bias and excitation can usually be applied alone to the tube, especially if a grid leak resistor is used. Plate voltage can be applied to the tetrode and pentode before the screen voltage with or without excitation to the control grid. NEVER APPLY SCREEN VOLTAGE BEFORE PLATE VOLTAGE. The only exception would be when the tube is cut off so that no space current (screen or plate current) will flow, or when the excitation and screen voltage are low. If screen voltage is applied before the plate voltage and screen current can flow, the maximum allowable screen dissipation will almost always be exceeded and tube damage will result.

Figure 28 is a chart for the protection of a triode tube. This chart covers the grid driven triode amplifier and the high-μ (zero bias) cathode driven triode amplifier. Drive voltage must never be applied to a zero-bias triode amplifier without plate voltage being applied.

CIRCUIT FAILURE	TRIODE		ZERO-BIASED TRIODE
	FIXED GRID BIAS	RESISTOR GRID BIAS	
Loss of Excitation	No Protection Required	Plate Over-Current Relay	No Protection Required
Loss of Antenna Loading	RF Output Detector & Relay	RF Output Detector & Relay	Grid Over-Current Relay
Excess Antenna Loading	RF Output Detector & Relay	RF Output Detector & Relay	RF Output Detector & Relay
Failure of Plate Supply	No Protection Required	No Protection Required	Grid Over-Current Relay
Failure of Grid Bias Supply	Plate Over-Current Relay	—	—

Figure 28. Triode protection chart

This chart indicates the location of a suitable relay which should act to remove the principal supply voltage from the stage or transmitter to prevent damage to the tube or transmitter.

3.10 *KEYING*

The tetrode and pentode power amplifier can be keyed using the same basic principles employed with any power amplifier. In addition, the screen electrode provides another low power circuit where keying can be introduced. Suitable filters must be used so that the make and break is slow enough to avoid high frequency sidebands known as "key clicks." The usual "key click" filter techniques apply.

There are several good methods of controlling the tetrode and pentode r-f power amplifier when exciter keying is used. With the screen voltage fixed and with fixed bias greater than cut-off, the tube will pass no current when the excitation is removed. A low or medium-μ triode amplifier can be keyed in the same manner. With the high-μ (zero bias) triodes, it is even simpler. When the drive is removed, the plate current falls to the normal, safe quiescent plate current.

It is also possible to key the exciter stage when the screen voltage for a tetrode or pentode is obtained through a dropping resistor and grid leak bias is used (see Figure 29A). In this system a high transconductance, low-μ triode is connected between screen and cathode, and the controlling bias for the

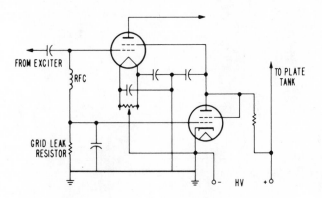

Figure 29A. Screen voltage control circuit for exciter keying or protection against loss of excitation when supplying screen from high voltage source.

small triode is taken from the tetrode or pentode bias developed in the grid leak resistor. When normal excitation is present on the r-f amplifier and grid bias is developed, the triode control tube is cut off and the screen voltage circuit operates normally. If excitation voltage is removed from the tetrode or pentode power amplifier, the bias voltage developed in the resistor drops to zero and the control triode becomes conducting. The current drawn by the triode control tube will increase the voltage drop across the series screen resistor and lower the screen voltage to a very low value.

There is still some voltage on the tetrode or pentode screen and a small static plate current flows. Usually this remaining current is not enough for the plate dissipation rating to be exceeded. This value can be reduced further by the use of a second control triode in parallel with the first (this redundancy is also insurance against failure of the single triode), by putting a gas regulator tube in series with the lead to the screen before the screen r-f by-pass capacitor, or by introducing a small amount of fixed bias on the power amplifier between the grid resistor and the power tube grid.

Figure 29B shows a method of keying a tetrode or pentode r-f power amplifier where the low voltage power supply for the screen of the power tube and for the plate and screen of the driver stage is keyed directly. This permits keying in a relatively low voltage, low current circuit. The key click filter capacitor, resistor, and choke are simple and assure positive control of the keying waveshape.

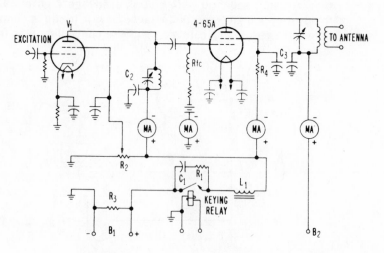

Figure 29B. A typical method of keying a tetrode or pentode amplifier.

3.11 AMPLITUDE MODULATION

A triode r-f amplifier can be plate; grid- or cathode-modulated Plate modulation is the type most extensively used. A triode may also be operated under a linear set of conditions for amplifying an amplitude modulated driver.

A tetrode or pentode r-f amplifier can be plate and screen, screen grid, control grid or cathode-modulated. Usually the system chosen is a combination of any of the previously listed

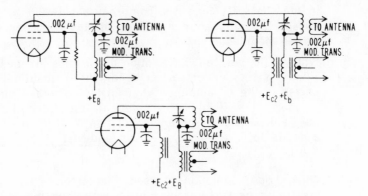

Figure 30. Basic screen and plate modulation circuits.

techniques. The most extensively used technique is a combination of plate and screen modulation. Often additional modulation must be provided on the control grid to reach 100 per cent modulation on the positive peaks. Figure 30 shows three of the basic plate and screen modulation circuits.

In plate and screen modulation it is necessary to introduce not only amplitude modulation of the plate voltage, but also to develop 70 to 100 per cent amplitude modulation of the screen voltage for 100 per cent carrier modulation. Modulation of the screen voltage can be developed in one of the following three ways:

(a) By supplying the screen voltage through a dropping resistor connected to the unmodulated d-c plate supply.

(b) When a low voltage fixed screen supply is used, a modulation choke is placed in series with the supply. In the case of voice modulation, this is about a 5 to 10 henry choke.

(c) A third winding on the modulation transformer designed to develop the required screen modulation voltage.

It is interesting to note that in all three cases the screen of the tetrode or pentode tube supplies the necessary audio power. During the portion of the modulation cycle, when the plate voltage is increased, the screen current decreases. If the screen is supplied through an impedance, such as the screen dropping resistor of a modulation choke, the voltage drop in this series impedance becomes less and the screen voltage rises in the desired manner. On the part of the modulation cycle when the plate voltage is decreased, the screen current increases causing a greater voltage drop in the screen series impedance and thus lowering the voltage on the screen of the tube. The screen by-pass capacitor value in the Class C stage is a compromise between good r-f by-passing and the shunting effect of this capacitance on the screen modulation circuit.

Where 100 per cent modulation capabilities are desired, the tube efficiency under carrier conditions is about half that expected in the r-f amplifier when plate and screen modulation is used. This efficiency is usually on the order of 35 to 40 per cent. Grid and screen modulation is used when there is a desire to save on physical size and cost of the modulation source.

When grid modulation is used, the screen voltage and grid bias must be taken from sources with good regulation. This usually means a separate low voltage power supply source. In the case of screen modulation, the grid bias should be taken from a grid leak bias resistor to provide some drive modulation.

The output of a pentode Class C amplifier can be controlled by applying to the suppressor grid a modulating voltage superimposed upon a suitable bias. As the suppressor grid in such an arrangement becomes more negative, the minimum instantaneous plate potential at which current can be drawn to the plate is increased. Thus, as the modulation varies the suppressor-grid potential, the output varies.

The suppressor-grid modulated amplifier has about the same plate efficiency as the grid modulated Class C amplifier. The overall efficiency is somewhat less because of the screen-grid losses. The modulating power is about the same. The linearity of modulation is not particularly high.

The screen-grid losses are higher because as the plate potential decreases, the current to the screen increases. This tendency toward high screen losses is the factor that usually limits the output power obtainable from a suppressor-grid modulated amplifier.

3.12   POWER SUPPLY CONSIDERATION

The power supply requirements for a triode are straightforward. The degree of regulation and ripple depends upon the requirements of the system. In the case of a linear r-f amplifier, it is important to have good plate power supply regulation. Without good regulation, the plate voltage will drop during the time the plate is conducting current heavily. This tendency for the voltage to drop will cause "flat topping" and will appear as distortion in the output. In a push-pull audio application where grid current flows, it is important to keep the grid circuit resistance to a minimum. If this is not done, positive peak clipping will occur. In the case of the tetrode and pentode, the need for screen voltage introduces some new considerations and provides some new possibilities.

Voltage for the screen grid of a low power tetrode or pentode can readily be taken from the power supply used for the plate of the tube. In this case, a series resistor, or potential dividing resistor, is chosen so that with the intended screen current flowing the voltage drop through the resistor is adequate to give the desired screen voltage. The potential dividing resistor is the preferred technique for those tubes with significant secondary screen emission (see Figure 6).

It is possible to take the screen voltage from a low voltage supply, frequently using an already available source in the equipment. There is considerable latitude so that an available voltage can be used. Sometimes a combination might be employed, where a dropping resistor is used in conjunction with a low voltage or intermediate voltage supply. Frequently a combination of series resistor and voltage source can be chosen so that the rated screen dissipation will not be exceeded regardless of the variations in screen current. With a fixed screen supply, there are advantages in using an appreciable amount of fixed grid bias so as to provide protection against loss of excitation, or for cases where the driver stage is being keyed.

If the screen voltage is taken through a dropping resistor from the plate supply, there is usually little point in using a fixed grid bias because an unreasonable amount of bias would be required to protect the tube if the excitation failed. When a screen dropping resistor is used, most of the bias is normally supplied through a grid resistor and other means are used for tube protection.

Under operating conditions with normal screen voltage, the cutoff bias is low (screen voltage divided by the screen μ). When a stage loses excitation and runs statically, the screen current falls close to zero. (See static curves of tube in question.) If the screen voltage is obtained through a simple dropping resistor from the plate supply, the screen voltage will then rise close to full plate voltage. Because the cutoff bias required is proportional to the screen voltage, the grid bias required will be much greater than the amount of bias desired under normal operating conditions.

The power output from a tetrode or pentode is very sensitive to screen voltage. For this reason, any application requiring a high degree of linearity through the amplifier requires a well regulated screen power supply. A screen dropping resistor from the plate supply is not recommended in such applications.

The suppressor grid power supply requirements are quite similar to the control grid power supply. The suppressor grid intercepts very little current, and therefore a low power supply may be used. Any variation in suppressor voltage due to ripple or lack of regulation will appear in the output of the amplifier due to the suppressor grid modulation of the plate current.

3.13 STABILIZING THE AMPLIFIER

3.13.1 Testing for parasitic oscillations

In the case of an r-f amplifier, it will be necessary to investigate not only the possibility of self-oscillation, but also lack of feedback on the fundamental frequency. The basic steps of checking for self-oscillation are threefold:

(a) The amplifier should be operated without r-f excitation and without fixed grid bias, with light loading and with low voltages applied to the plate and to the screen of a tetrode or pentode.

The voltage should be high enough to develop full plate dissipation. For this test, grid leak bias should be used. If the screen and plate voltage supplied cannot be adjusted directly to low voltages, suitable series resistance should be used, either in series with the rectifier output or transformer primary so that the voltages developed at the tube will be low.

Light bulbs of the correct size will serve as resistors in series with the primary of the rectifier transformers. The r-f circuits should be tuned off-resonance to see if self-oscillation of the amplifier can be started. The indication of any current by the grid milliammeter means that self-oscillation is present.

(b) The frequency of the self-oscillation must be determined. A simple neon bulb will indicate whether the frequency of oscillation is high or low. The lower the frequency the more orange will be the glow. A purple color indicates a VHF or UHF oscillation. With a little experience, it will become possible to guess the approximate frequency very closely. A wavemeter or an oscilloscope will then determine the exact frequency.

(c)   After the frequency of oscillation is measured, it remains to identify the circuit supporting the oscillation. The circuit must then be altered without disturbing the performance of the amplifier on the normal frequency of the amplifier.

3.13.2 Correction of Parasitic Oscillations

The usual self-oscillations in r-f power amplifiers have been found to fall in the following three classes:

(a)   Oscillation at VHF from about 40 MHz to 200 MHz, regardless of the normal frequency of the amplifier.

(b)   Self-oscillation on the fundamental frequency of the amplifier.

(c)   Oscillation at a low radio frequency below the normal frequency of the amplifier.

The low frequency oscillation in an amplifier usually involves the r-f chokes, especially when chokes are used in both the output and input circuits.

Oscillation near the fundamental frequency involves the normal resonant circuits, and brings up the question of neutralizing the r-f power amplifier. This general subject is discussed under "Neutralization," Section (5).

When a parasitic self-oscillation is found on a very high frequency, the interconnecting leads of the tube, the tuning capacitor and the by-pass capacitors are involved. This type of oscillation does not usually occur when the power amplifier is designed for operation in the VHF region and where the r-f circuits external to the tube have negligibly small tuning capacitors. Without tuning capacitors, the highest frequency oscillating circuit possible is then the fundamental, and there would be no higher frequency circuit available for the parasitic. The only exception would be where higher order modes of transmission line circuits might provide a parasitic circuit.

The VHF oscillation occurs commonly in amplifier constructions where the radio frequency circuits are coils and capacitors, as in the HF and LF region, in audio amplifiers or voltage regulators. As in Figure 31, the parasitic oscillation uses the capacitors and the associated grid and plate leads for the inductances of the parasitic circuit. The tube capacitances help form the tuned-plate tuned-grid oscillation circuits. The circuit is indicated by the heavy lines in Figure 31.

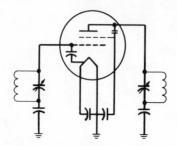

Figure 31. Usual circuit supporting VHF parasitic oscillation in HF r-f amplifiers.

There are several straightforward ways to suppress VHF parasitic oscillation. In general, it will probably be more easily suppressed if the general layout and by-passing methods indicated earlier are followed.

It turns out that the frequency usually met in a VHF parasitic oscillation is well above the self-neutralizing frequency of the tube (see Section 5). However, if the self-neutralizing frequency of the tube can be increased and the frequency of the parasitic lowered, complete suppression of the parasitic may result, or its suppression by resistor-coil parasitic suppressors may be made easier.

It is also possible to predict fairly closely with a grid dip wavemeter the parasitic frequency to be expected in a given equipment. The circuit should be complete and with no voltages on the tube. Couple the meter to the plate or screen lead and determine the resonant frequency. The following two methods of eliminating the VHF parasitic oscillation have been used successfully:

(a) By placing a small coil and resistor combination in the plate lead between the plate of the tube and the tank circuit (see Figure 32). The resistor-coil combination is usually made up of a non-inductive resistor of about 25 to 100 ohms, shunted by three or four turns approximately one-half inch in diameter and frequently wound right around the resistor. In some cases it may be necessary to use such a suppressor in both the plate and grid leads. The resistor-coil combination operates on the principle that

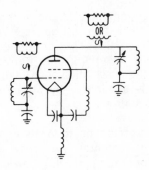

Figure 32. Placement of parasitic suppressors to eliminate VHF parasitic oscillations in HF r-f
amplifiers.

the resistor loads the VHF circuit but is shunted by
the coil for the lower fundamental frequency. In the
process of adjusting the resistor-coil combination,
it is often found that the resistor runs too hot. The
heat is usually caused by the dissipation of fundamental power in the resistor. This is an indication of
too many turns in the suppressor coil. Just enough
turns should be used to suppress the parasitic and
no more. Once the parasitic has been suppressed
there will be no parasitic voltage or current present.
Therefore, there is no parasitic power to be dissipated.

(b)   By the use of small parasitic chokes in the plate lead
(see Figure 32). The size of this coil will vary considerably depending upon the tube and the circuit
layout, and may run from about four to ten turns
of about a one-half inch diameter. The presence of
this choke in the frequency determining part of the
circuit lowers the frequency of a possible VHF parasitic so that it falls near the self-neutralizing frequency of the tube and by-pass leads. In addition to
varying the size of the suppressor choke, the amount
of inductance common to the screen and filament in
the filament grounding strap may be a factor. This
can be varied simultaneously with the suppressor
choke.

Of the two methods indicated above for suppressing VHF
parasitic oscillations, the first one is probably the simpler to
use and has been widely employed.

The procedure of checking for self-oscillation in an r-f power
amplifier described previously will normally show up most
trouble and allow for its correction. If, however, the correction

53

is marginal, it may sometimes happen that under operating conditions the self-oscillation will be triggered off. The oscillation may occur only on the peaks of amplitude modulation or on keying surges. By observing the r-f envelope on a cathode ray oscilloscope, the oscillation can usually be seen. The trouble can be fully eliminated by pursuing further the outlined corrective procedure.

A more difficult self-oscillation to locate is one occurring on a harmonic of the fundamental frequency and occurring only when the stage is operating. It will show up when testing for the presence of abnormal power in the harmonics under operating conditions.

In the case of an audio amplifier employing tetrodes or pentodes, small non-inductive resistors of about 100 ohms resistance should be placed in series with the plate, and possibly the grid as well, in case self-oscillation of the amplifier occurs in the very high frequency portion of the r-f spectrum. Should the audio or d-c voltage drop in the resistor be objectionable, it can be shunted with a small coil.

Another form of commonly encountered self-oscillation is known as "dynatron" oscillation. Dynatron oscillation is caused when any electrode in a vacuum tube has negative resistance. Secondary emission characteristics of the screen grid in a tetrode were discussed in Section 2.2; it was pointed out that at times there may be more electrons leaving the screen grid than are arriving. If the screen voltage is allowed to increase under these conditions, even more electrons will leave the grid; the phenomenon implies a negative resistance characteristic. If there is high alternating current impedance in the circuit from the screen grid through the screen grid power supply, and from the plate power supply to the plate, dynatron oscillation may be sustained.

Dynatron oscillation typically occurs in the region of one to 20 Hz. This low-frequency oscillation is usually accompanied by another oscillation in the 1000-2000 kHz region. Suppression of these oscillations can be accomplished by placing a large bypass capacitor (1000 μF) across the output of the screen grid power supply. The circuit supporting the oscillation can also be detuned by a large inductor. Increasing the circuit losses at the frequency of oscillation is also effective.

SECTION 4
LINEAR AMPLIFIER
AND SINGLE SIDEBAND SERVICE

4.1 WHY SINGLE SIDEBAND

The increase in commercial and military communication traffic has become so great that a need exists for faster, more reliable, spectrum-conserving systems. **Single-sideband** (SSB) operation meets this need and makes more efficient use of the available spectrum.

The advantages of single-sideband transmission over conventional amplitude-modulated transmission have been discussed in literature [7, 8, 9, 10] and are summarized as follows:

1. The bandwidth requirement of the transmitted signal is less than half that of conventional double-sideband systems. For example, if a signal carrying the normal speech spectrum of 200 to 3000 Hz is transmitted via conventional amplitude-modulation-with-carrier systems the bandwidth required is twice the highest frequency being transmitted, or 6000 Hz. Elimination of the carrier and one sideband (neither of which is essential to the transmission of intelligence) permits the bandwidth to be reduced to 2800 Hz (Figure 33). The audio improvement in intelligence is enhanced because of the elimination of interfering audio heterodynes caused by adjacent channel signals.

---

7 J. F. Honey, "Performance of AM and SSB Communications," Tele-Tech. September, 1953.
8 Fundamentals of Single Sideband, Collins Radio Company, September, 1960.
9 E. W. Pappenfus, Warren B. Bruene, and E. O. Schoenike, Single Sideband Principles and Circuits, New York, McGraw-Hill, 1964.
10 Proceedings of the I.R.E. (Single Sideband Issue), December, 1956.

Figure 33. Relative spectrum space occupied by AM signal and SSB signal modulated by frequencies of 200 to 3000 Hz.

2. The narrower frequency band required for SSB operation allows bandwidth reduction of the selective circuits in the receiver to only that width needed to receive the signal without distortion. While there is some improvement in signal-to-noise ratio, the greatest improvement is the reduction in the strength (at the detector) of some of the interfering signals which would otherwise be admitted with the wider passband.

3. A relatively high level of information-bearing sideband power can be obtained without the use of a high-power modulator. This permits a lower average power in the final radio-frequency stage, and substantial reductions in total power input, total weight, and total cost of the transmitting equipment.

4. SSB operation greatly reduces the audio distortion often encountered over long-path transmissions using conventional amplitude-modulated signals.

4.2   RATING TUBES FOR LINEAR AMPLIFIER SERVICE

The power-handling capability of a given tube in single-sideband service depends upon the nature of the signal being transmitted and the power dissipating capability. In addition, the method of establishing single-sideband service ratings should be such that relatively simple test equipment can be used to determine whether or not a tube is operating within its maximum ratings.

It is impractical to establish a rating based on voice-signal modulation because of the irregular waveforms encountered and the varying ratios of peak-to-average signal power found in various voices. The most convenient rating method, and probably the most practical, employs a single-tone driving signal (such as that from a sine-wave audio-signal generator) to modulate the SSB transmitter. By using this test signal at its full modulation capability, the amplifier will operate under steady, maximum-signal conditions which are easily duplicated and observed.

When a single sine-wave tone modulates a single-sideband transmitter, the r-f output seen on an oscilloscope (Figure 34a) appears as a steady, unmodulated signal (resembling an un-modulated AM carrier) because the output is a continuous signal having a frequency removed from that of the carrier by the modulating frequency, as shown in Figure 34b.

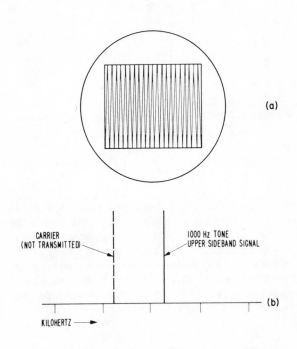

(a)

CARRIER
(NOT TRANSMITTED)

1000 Hz TONE
UPPER SIDEBAND SIGNAL

(b)

KILOHERTZ ——▶

Figure 34. R-F output of SSB transmitter with single-tone modulation. (a) Oscilloscope pattern (b) Spectrum for 1000-Hz tone

Consequently, the operation of a linear amplifier under single-tone modulation is comparable to that of a telegraph trans-mitter under key-down conditions. As such, the performance of the stage at maximum signal (or peak) conditions can be ascertained by meter readings. However, this simple test lacks information on the linearity of the stage. To study linearity thoroughly by observing the amplifier output, some means must be provided to vary the output level from zero to maximum signal with a regular pattern that is easily interpreted. A simple means is to use two audio tones of equal amplitude to modulate the single-sideband transmitter. This is termed a **two-tone** test. This procedure causes the transmitter to emit two steady signals separated by the frequency difference of the two audio tones (Figure 35).

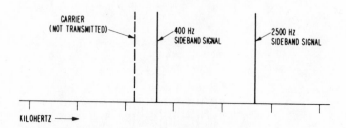

Figure 35. Spectrum of SSB transmitter modulated by two-tone test signal containing 400- and 2500-Hz tones and transmitting upper sideband.

In some single-sideband generators, this type of signal is obtained by impressing a single tone at the audio input and injecting the carrier (by unbalancing a balanced modulator) to provide the second equal amplitude r-f signal (Figure 36). The resultant, or beat between the two r-f signals, produces a pattern which, when observed on an oscilloscope, has the appearance of a carrier, 100 per cent amplitude modulated by a series of half sine waves as shown in Figure 37.

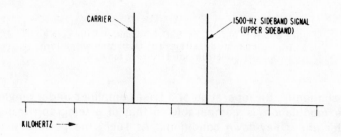

Figure 36. Spectrum of SSB transmitter modulated by 1500-Hz tone and injecting carrier to obtain second r-f signal equal in amplitude to tone.

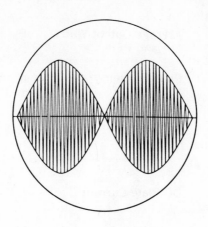

Figure 37. R-f output of SSB transmitter modulated by two-tone test signal as seen on the oscilloscope.

When measuring the distortion of a linear r-f amplifier or a chain of linear r-f amplifiers by the two-tone technique, it is sometimes more expedient to use two r-f signal sources separated in frequency by the desired number of hertz, and then to combine them in a manner which will minimize the interaction of the two signals. The two r-f signals represent the two equivalent sideband frequencies generated by the two-audio-tone system and when viewed on an oscilloscope appear exactly the same.

A linear amplifier is usually rated at peak envelope input or output power level. **Peak envelope power** (PEP) is the root-mean-square (rms) power generated at the peak of the modulation envelope. With either a two-equal-tone test signal or a single-tone test signal, the following equations approximate the relationships between single-tone and two-tone meter readings, peak envelope power, and average power for Class B or Class AB operation.

4.2.1 Single Tone

DC Plate Current $\qquad I_b = \dfrac{i_{pm}}{\pi}$ (1)

Plate Input Watts $\qquad P_{in} = \dfrac{i_{pm} E_b}{\pi}$ (2)

Average Output Watts and PEP	$P_o = \dfrac{i_{pm}e_p}{4}$	(3)
Plate Efficiency	$\eta_p = \dfrac{\pi e_p}{4E_b}$	(4)

4.2.2 Two Equal Tones

DC Plate Current	$I_b = \dfrac{2\,i_{pm}}{\pi^2}$	(5)
Plate Input Watts	$P_{in} = \dfrac{2\,i_{pm}E_b}{\pi^2}$	(6)
Average Output Watts	$P_o = \dfrac{i_{pm}e_p}{8}$	(7)
PEP Watts	$P_o = \dfrac{i_{pm}e_p}{4}$	(8)
Plate Efficiency	$\eta_p = \left(\dfrac{\pi}{4}\right)^2 \dfrac{e_p}{E_b}$	(9)

4.2.3 Definition of Symbols:

i_{pm} = Peak of the plate current pulse — the plate current pulse is not sinusoidal.

e_p = Peak value of plate swing, assumed to be sinusoidal when plate tank "Q" is sufficiently high.

π = 3.14

E_b = d-c plate voltage

The approximate equations given above are for single-tone and two-tone conditions, the most common test situations. In some multi-channel transmitter applications, many more tones are used and the following method will determine the peak-envelope-power to average-power ratio. For the purposes of this explanation, it is assumed that all the tones are equal, however, unequal tones can be employed with this technique.

The following examples demonstrate two important relationships of single and multitone signals amplified by a linear system.

1. The amplifier is set up for a single-tone driving signal and a Point "A" (see Figure 38) on the operating line is established. A definite PEP output is developed under this condition. To drive this linear amplifier to the same PEP output with a multitone signal, the drive signal voltage for each tone must be 1/nth (n = number of tones) the amplitude of the single-tone signal.

2. By assuming a perfectly linear amplifier wherein the input signal waveshape is exactly reproduced in the output load, these grid waveshapes can be used to demonstrate the relationship of PEP to Average Power.

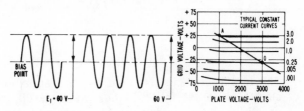

Figure 38. Single-tone condition.

4.2.4 Single-Tone Signal

$$P_{avg} = \frac{E_{1(rms)}^2}{R_L} = \frac{\left(\frac{60}{\sqrt{2}}\right)^2}{R_L} = \frac{1800}{R_L} \; W \qquad (10)$$

$$PEP = \frac{E_{1(rms)}^2}{R_L} = \frac{\left(\frac{60}{\sqrt{2}}\right)^2}{R_L} = \frac{1800}{R_L} \; W \qquad (11)$$

Therefore, $PEP = P_{avg}$ \qquad\qquad (12)

4.2.5 Two-Tone Signal

$$P_{avg} = P_{1\,avg} + P_{2\,avg} \qquad (13)$$

$$= \frac{\left(E_{1(rms)}\right)^2}{R_L} + \frac{\left(E_{2(rms)}\right)^2}{R_L}$$

$$= \frac{\left(\frac{30}{\sqrt{2}}\right)^2}{R_L} + \frac{\left(\frac{30}{\sqrt{2}}\right)^2}{R_L}$$

$$= \frac{450}{R_L} + \frac{450}{R_L} = \frac{900}{R_L} \; W$$

$$PEP = \frac{(E_{1rms} + E_{2rms})^2}{R_L} \qquad (14)$$

$$= \frac{\left(\frac{30}{\sqrt{2}} + \frac{30}{\sqrt{2}}\right)^2}{R_L}$$

$$= \frac{\left(\frac{60}{\sqrt{2}}\right)^2}{R_L} = \frac{1800}{R_L} \text{ W}$$

Therefore, $PEP = 2 \times P_{avg}$ $\qquad (15)$

The two frequencies (f_1 and f_2) are equal in amplitude but slightly different in frequency. As a result, when they are exactly in phase, the two crest voltages add directly to produce the crest of the two-tone envelope. When the two frequencies are exactly out of phase, then the cusp of the two-tone envelope results (see Figure 39). Note that the voltage amplitude at the crest of the resultant two-tone envelope is equal to that of the single-tone envelope and therefore the tube is driven to the same point "A" on the operating line in each case. If the tube is driven to the same peak plate current and the same peak plate voltage swing by different exciting signals, then the Peak Envelope Power Output for both signals is the same.

4.2.6   Three-Tone Signal

$$P_{avg} = P_{1\,avg} + P_{2\,avg} + P_{3\,avg} \qquad (16)$$

$$= \frac{(E_{1rms})^2}{R_L} + \frac{(E_{2rms})^2}{R_L} + \frac{(E_{3rms})^2}{R_L}$$

$$= \frac{\left(\frac{20}{\sqrt{2}}\right)^2}{R_L} + \frac{\left(\frac{20}{\sqrt{2}}\right)^2}{R_L} + \frac{\left(\frac{20}{\sqrt{2}}\right)^2}{R_L}$$

$$= \frac{200}{R_L} + \frac{200}{R_L} + \frac{200}{R_L} = \frac{600}{R_L} \text{ W}$$

$$PEP = \frac{(E_{1rms} + E_{2rms} + E_{3rms})^2}{R_L} \qquad (17)$$

$$= \frac{\left(\frac{20}{\sqrt{2}} + \frac{20}{\sqrt{2}} + \frac{20}{\sqrt{2}}\right)^2}{R_L}$$

$$= \frac{\left(\frac{60}{\sqrt{2}}\right)^2}{R_L} = \frac{1800}{R_L} \text{ W}$$

Therefore, $PEP = 3 \times P_{avg}$ \qquad (18)

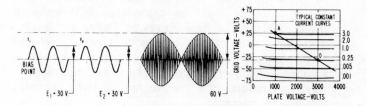

Figure 39. Two-tone condition.

Note that the sum of the three individual tone crest exciting voltages add in phase to drive the tube to the same peak current and peak plate voltage swing as that of the single-tone case (see Figure 40). The PEP output will therefore be the same as for the single-tone and two-tone examples.

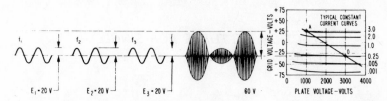

Figure 40. Three-tone condition.

The above results for equal amplitude tones may be summarized by the following expressions:

$$PEP = n\, P_{avg} \qquad (19)$$

and \qquad $PEP = n^2 \times P_t$ \qquad (20)

where \qquad P_{avg} = average power of composite signal

P_t = average power in each tone

n = number of tones

Example:

An FM mobile radiotelephone mountain-top repeater is to be designed to simultaneously rebroadcast one to eight channels. Each channel must have an average power output of 100 watts. How much Peak Envelope Power must the linear amplifier deliver?

Each channel can be considered to be a single-tone signal. Therefore, the PEP of each channel is equal to the average power of each channel. The **maximum power output** requirement of the amplifier will be under the 8-tone condition. The average power output for the composite 8-tone signal will be 8 times the 100 watts-per-channel power. Therefore, the linear amplifier must be capable of 800 watts of average power output. The Peak Envelope Power will be 8 times the average power of the composite signal ($PEP = nP_{avg}$) or 6400 watts. A tube must be selected to deliver this peak-envelope and average power at an intermodulation distortion level compatible with the degree of interchannel cross-talk that can be tolerated.

4.3 SELECTION OF TUBES FOR SINGLE SIDEBAND SERVICE

As a guide in selecting tubes for various power levels of single-sideband service, typical operating conditions for various EIMAC tubes are included in this section. These data give values at the maximum signal condition for sustained single-tone modulation, and also give the average current values (as read on a d-c meter) using a two-tone test signal adjusted to the same peak envelope power as the single-tone condition. Voice-signal average currents will, of course, be lower than the two-tone condition by an amount depending upon the peak-to-average ratio of the voice signal, which is less than that of a two-tone signal in all cases. Typical third- and fifth-order intermodulation distortion product levels for maximum drive conditions are also given for the two-tone condition.

Tube Type	Plate Voltage Vdc	Screen Voltage Vdc	Suppressor Voltage Vdc	Bias Voltage Vdc	Filament Voltage V	Filament Current A	Zero Signal Plate Current mA	Single Tone Plate Current mA	Two Tone Plate Current mA	Useful PEP Output w	3rd Order Distortion Products db	5th Order Distortion Products* db	Class of Service	Resonant Plate Load
3-400Z	2000 2500 3000	— — —	— — —	0 0 0	5.0	14.5	62 84 100	400 400 333	265 270 238	445 520 655	-32 -29 -27	-35 -36 -34	AB1 AB1 AB1	2750 3200 5500
3-1000Z	2500 3000	— —	— —	0 0	7.5	21.3	162 240	800 670	550 468	1050 1080	-32 -29	-39 -37	AB1 AB1	1760 2650
3CX1000A7	2500	—	—	0	5.0	33	270	800	560	1270	-32	-38	AB1	1650
3CX10,000A3	6000 7000	— —	— —	-270 -325	7.5	104	500 500	4000 4000	— —	8000 20,000	— —	— —	AB1 AB1	1020 1135
3CX10,000A7	7000 7000	— —	— —	0 0	7.5	104	600 600	3720 5000	— —	17,700 24,000	— —	— —	AB1 AB1	1020 1745
4CX250B	2000	325	—	-56	6.0	2.9	90	277	196	348	-25	-25	AB1	4500
4CX250R	2000	400	—	-72	6.0	2.9	95	322	225	475	-25	-35	AB1	4000
4CX300A	2000	325	—	-56	6.0	3.9	90	277	196	348	-25	-25	AB1	4500
4CX300Y	2000	400	—	-72	6.0	3.9	100	312	222	423	-28	-30	AB1	3500
4CX350A	2200	300	—	-20	6.0	3.6	100	215	167	318	-29	-30	AB1	6000
4CX350F	2200	300	—	-20	26.5	0.81	100	215	167	318	-29	-30	AB1	6000
4CX600A	2000 2500	400 300	—	-50 -31	6.0	4.8	200 200	465 400	343 304	500 524	-30 -32	-47 -41	AB1 AB1	2000 4100
4CX1000A/K	3000	310	—	-63	6.0	9.9	250	750	540	1400	-23	-26	AB1	2200
4CX1500B	2500 2750 2900	225 225 225	—	-34 -34 -34	6.0	9.9	300 300 300	720 755 710	530 555 542	890 1100 1100	-40 -41 -44	-47 -48 -48	AB1 AB1 AB1	1900 1900 2200
4CX3000A	5000	850	—	-180	9.0	43.5	500	1650	1100	5300	-32	-35	AB1	1700
4CX5000A	5000 7500	1000 1250	—	-210 -307	7.5	78	670 450	1670 1900	1240 1590	5260 11,910	-36 -24	-36 -34	AB1 AB1	1790 1580
4CX5000R	5000 7500	1000 1250	—	-197 -300	7.5	78	800 500	2010 1900	1460 —	5700 10,000	-35	-40	AB1 AB1	1450 2460
4CX10,000D	7500 7500	1350 1500	—	-262 -340	7.5	78	900 500	2300 3330	1770 —	11,022 15,950	-35	-42	AB1 AB1	1600 2250
4CX15,000A	7000 7500 10,000	1250 1500 1500	—	-240 -350 -370	6.3	168	1500 1000 1000	3090 4400 4250	2380 —	11,300 20,800 28,500	-49	-45	AB1 AB1 AB1	1350 865 1260
5-500A	2000 3000 4000	750 750 750	0 0 0	-100 -112 -121	10.0	10	150 100 80	338 320 322	252 221 212	395 612 832	-52 -33 -28	-49 -41 -37	AB1 AB1 AB1	3600 5800 7700
5CX1500A	2500 3000 4000	500 500 500	0 0 0	-87 -89 -90	5.0	40	250 250 250	660 690 690	468 482 485	1090 1330 1785	-38 -36 -33	-39 -41 -42	AB1 AB1 AB1	2340 3000 4000
5CX3000A	4000 6000 6000	800 700 800	0 0 -160	-142 -128 -137	9.0	43.5	500 450 450	1570 1340 1475	1100 950 1025	3820 4910 5870	-40 -39 -40	-43 -45 -43	AB1 AB1 AB1	1550 2825 2330

The intermodulation distortion products will be as specified or better for all levels from zero signal to maximum output power and are referenced against one tone of a two equal tone signal.

4.3.1 Intermodulation Distortion

In general, the criteria used in the selection of operating parameters for tubes in high-fidelity audio-amplifier service are applicable when selecting the operating conditions for linear r-f amplifiers. In the case of the sideband linear amplifier, the degree of linearity of the stage is of considerable importance. Intermodulation distortion products in linear power-amplifier circuits can be caused by either amplitude gain nonlinearity or phase shift with change in input signal level. Intermodulation distortion products appear only when the r-f signal has a varying envelope amplitude. A single continuous-frequency wave will be amplified a fixed amount and shifted in phase a fixed amount. The nonlinearity of the amplifier will produce only harmonics of the input wave. If the input r-f wave changes at an audio rate, however, the nonlinearity of the amplifier will cause undesirable intermodulation distortion products to appear. Previously, it was pointed out that a two-tone signal offers a convenient means of measuring distortion. If these two r-f tones are equal in amplitude, the resultant signal envelope varies from zero to maximum, so that this signal can be used to test an amplifier over its entire dynamic amplitude range.

When an r-f signal with varying amplitude is passed through a nonlinear device, many new products are produced. The frequency and amplitude of each component can be determined mathematically since the nonlinear device can be represented by a power series expanded about the zero-signal operating point. An excellent mathematical discussion of intermodulation distortion appears in "Single Sideband Principles and Circuits."[11]

An example of a typical two-tone signal serves to summarize this mathematical presentation. Assume that two equal amplitude test signals (f_1 = 2.001 MHz and f_2 = 2.003 MHz) are applied to a linear amplifier. Figure 41 shows the output spectrum of the device.

Many of the distortion-product currents are seen to fall outside the passband of the amplifier tuned circuits. If no impedance exists at the frequencies of the distortion component, then no voltage can be developed. Further study of this spectrum discloses that no even-order products fall near the two desired signals. Some odd-order products, however, fall near

---

11 Pappenfus, et al, op. cit.

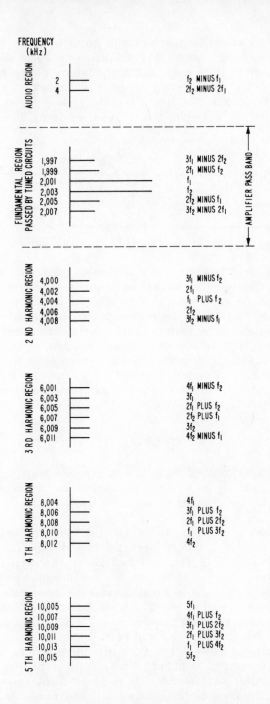

Figure 41. Spectrum at the output of a non-linear device with an input of two equal amplitude sine waves of $f_1 = 2.001$ MHz and $f_2 = 2.003$ MHz.

the desired frequencies and possibly within the passband of the tuned circuits. The distortion products which are usually given in tube data sheets are the third- and fifth-order inter-modulation-distortion products which can fall within the amplifier passband. Using the same f_1 and f_2 frequencies of the previous example, the frequencies of the third-order products are:

$$2f_1 - f_2 = 1.999 \text{ MHz}$$
$$2f_2 - f_1 = 2.005 \text{ MHz}$$

and the frequencies of the fifth-order products are:

$$3f_1 - 2f_2 = 1.997 \text{ MHz}$$
$$3f_2 - 2f_1 = 2.007 \text{ MHz}$$

These frequencies are well within the passband of a tuned circuit intended to pass voice frequencies and therefore power will be delivered to the antenna at these frequencies. **All intermodulation distortion power is wasted and serves no purpose other than to cause interference to adjacent channels.** The adjacent channels may be other services using nearby frequencies or other channels on the same transmitter. In any case, an interfering signal is created by the generation of distortion products in the (nearly) linear system.

4.3.2   What Makes A Tube Linear?

Intermodulation distortion in a power amplifier tube is mainly caused by its transfer characteristics. An ideal transfer-characteristic curve is shown in Figure 42.

Even-order products do not contribute to the intermodulation distortion problem because they fall outside the amplifier passband. Therefore, if the transfer characteristic produces an even-order curvature at the small-signal end of the curve (from Point A to Point B) and the remaining portion of the curve (Point B to Point C) is linear, the tube is considered to have an ideal transfer characteristic. If the operating point of the amplifier is set at Point 0 (located midway horizontally between Point A and Point B), there will be no distortion in a Class AB amplifier. However, no tube has this idealized transfer characteristic. It is possible, by clever manipulation of the electron ballistics within a given tube structure, to alter the transfer characteristic and minimize the distortion products. Several tubes developed recently at EIMAC have transfer characteristics which significantly reduce intermodulation distortion.

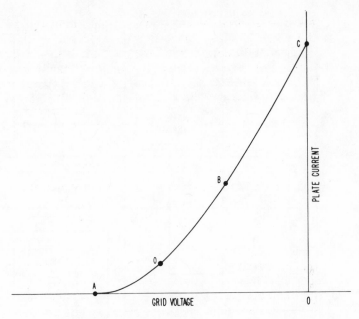

Figure 42. Ideal grid-plate transfer curve for Class AB operation.

4.3.3 A Two Tone Intermodulation Distortion Test Analyzer

The Intermodulation Distortion Test Console at EIMAC uses two separate r-f signal sources 2000 Hz apart. The two test signals are at 2.001 and 2.003 MHz. The signals are combined in a toroidal hybrid combiner and amplified by a 4CX5000A operating as a Class A amplifier. The 4CX5000A stage is loaded with a 50-ohm noninductive load in addition to the impedance of the input circuit of the tube under test. The test amplifier can evaluate many different tube types and is capable of all classes of operation. It may be grid-driven or cathode-driven. Distortion measuring equipment consists of a Panoramic SB-12A spectrum analyzer and a modified Hewlett-Packard HP-310A wave analyzer. Grid voltage swing is measured with a Tektronix "Z" amplifier and oscilloscope. Power output is measured with either an HP-410C vacuum-tube voltmeter or a John Fluke 910A rms voltmeter. The HP-410C is ideal since it responds to peak voltage and is calibrated in rms to provide an rms-voltage measurement at the peak of the r-f envelope. By properly measuring the voltage across the load, squaring it, and dividing by the load resistance, the peak envelope power and average power can both be measured directly (Figure 43).

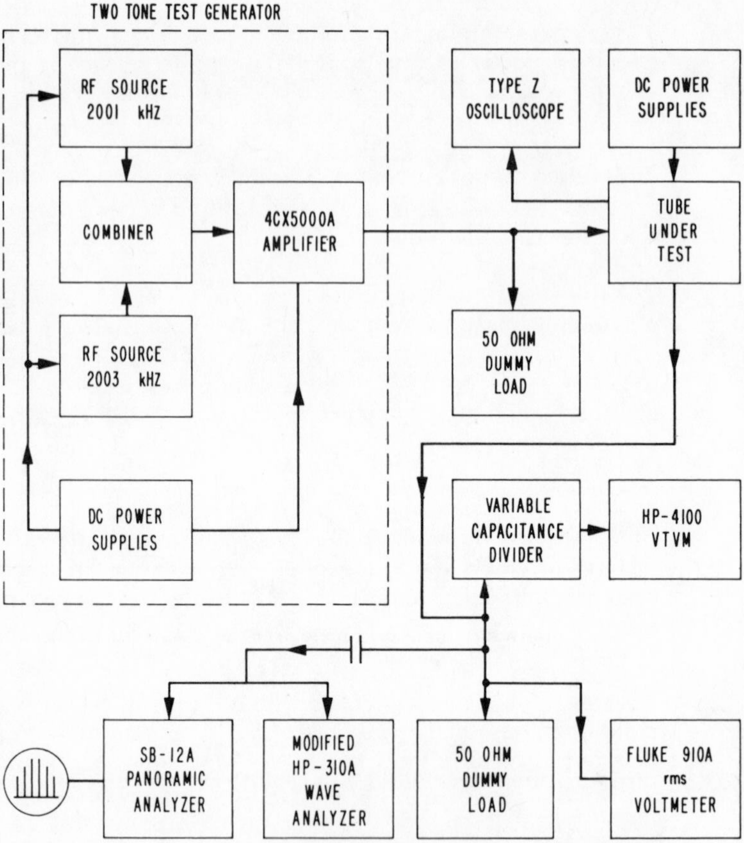

Figure 43. Block diagram of Intermodulation Distortion Analyzer. A low-distortion two-tone r-f signal is generated at 2 MHz and applied to the test amplifier. The output of the amplifier is dissipated in a dummy load and a portion of the output signal is examined on the screen of a high-resolution panoramic analyzer or tunable voltmeter. Distortion products as low as − 75 decibels below one tone of a two equal tone signal may be studied.

4.3.4   Standards of Measurement

To adequately describe the performance of a tube in single-sideband linear service, it is necessary to determine many parameters. The normal electrode voltages and currents must be specified plus the two-tone currents, the operating point, the peak envelope power (PEP), and the magnitude of the intermodulation-distortion products.

These parameters are defined as follows: The term **peak envelope power** is the root-mean-square power at the crest of the envelope. This term is usually shortened to PEP.

The idling plate current determined by the operating point is called the **zero-signal plate current** and is designated I_{bo}.

The other two plate current values of significance are the **single-tone plate current** and the **two-tone plate current.** The ratio of single-tone to two-tone current is 1.57:1 in a true Class B amplifier (180° plate conduction angle). For other classes of linear operation and for different zero-signal plate currents, this ratio may vary from 1.1:1 to 1.57:1.

The standard method of specifying the magnitude of the distortion products is to specify the reduction in decibels of one product from one tone of a two-equal-tone signal. For example:

Assume that a particular tube under a given set of operating conditions has third-order distortion products of −35 db and fifth-order distortion products of −50 db. This means the third-order product has an amplitude of 35 db below one of the two test tones and the fifth-order product has an amplitude 50 db below one of the two test tones. (It is also correct to add the amplitudes of the two third-order products and compare them to the **sum** of the two tones. The decibel ratio is still the same as the example.) It is **NOT** correct to compare one distortion product to the sum of the two tones; that is to say, the PEP value of the signal. The resulting distortion figure would be 6 db better than the correct example (−41 db rather than −35 db and −56 db rather than −50 db).

It is a normal test procedure to adjust the tube under test to the full drive condition and to measure all the pertinent parameters. The drive signal is then reduced in a predetermined manner. At each test point, all of the previously noted parameters are again measured. The resulting data can then be plotted as a function of drive voltage. It should be noted that maximum intermodulation distortion does not necessarily occur at maximum drive level, and it can be shown mathematically that an intermodulation characteristic like Figure 44 can be expected. There is very good correlation between mathematical prediction and actual test results.

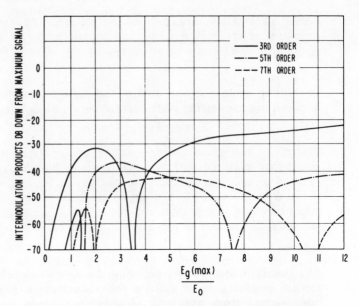

Figure 44. Intermodulation distortion products may be predicted mathematically. This universal family of IMD curves applies to all perfect tubes obeying the 3/2-power law. (See Section 6.4.) The curves are plots of IMD level (Y axis) referred to the driving signal expressed as a ratio of drive to operating bias. As the drive is increased, the various IMD products pass through maxima and minima. Misleading conclusions of amplifier performance may be drawn if the equipment happens to be tested near a cusp on the IMD curve, where a particular product drops to an extremely low level. The whole operating range of the equipment must be examined to draw a true picture of IMD performance.

4.4 ˜ LINEAR AMPLIFIER DESIGN

The following features are desirable for tubes used in r-f **linear** amplifier service, in addition to other elements discussed in Section 6, "Operating Conditions for Various Applications."

1. High power gain
2. Low plate-to-grid capacitance
3. Good efficiency
4. Linear characteristics which are maintained without degradation across the desired operating range.

For linear service, r-f amplifiers may be operated in Class A, AB_1, AB_2, or B modes. The choice of tube may be triode, tetrode, or pentode, either grid or cathode driven. The choice of mode, tube, and driving method will depend upon the operational specifications of each individual case.

4.4.1 The Triode Amplifier

The triode tube having a large plate-to-grid interelectrode capacitance always requires neutralization in grid-driven service to prevent oscillation. A triode having a low amplification factor is suitable for Class AB_1 and AB_2 grid-driven operation. The r-f grid excitation voltage for this type of service will be quite high and grid excursions into the positive region are normal for Class AB_2 service. A swamping resistor should be used across the input tuned circuit to maintain a constant input impedance to the stage and for stability. With a low value of swamping resistance, the grid current drawn is only a small part of the total grid load and the driver load impedance is relatively constant. The swamping resistor improves r-f stability by providing a low impedance to ground for regenerative feedback through the plate-to-grid capacitance.

The high-amplification-factor triode performs exceptionally well in circuits where the grid is grounded and the cathode is driven. Under these conditions, the control grid acts as a shield between the input and output circuits. Neutralization, therefore, is not normally required. EIMAC has developed a line of high amplification ("zero bias") triodes for cathode-driven linear-amplifier service, producing stage gains of 10 decibels or more. These tubes operate in the Class AB_2 mode and require only filament, plate, and drive power. For optimum linear operation, a tuned circuit is placed in the cathode r-f return path to maintain a sinusoidal waveshape over the drive cycle. The tuned circuit will reduce the intermodulation distortion produced by the amplifier and will also reduce drive-power requirements.

The tuned-cathode circuit can be the output circuit of the previous stage if it is located close to the amplifier stage. If, however, the amplifier is far removed and coupled by a length of coaxial cable, it is recommended that a tuned-cathode circuit with a "Q" of between two and four be used.

4.4.2 Tetrode and Pentode Amplifiers

Most tetrode and pentode amplifiers are designed to be grid driven to take advantage of the high power gain of these types. A grid swamping resistor should be used if the stage is to be driven into grid current, and the tetrode or pentode should be neutralized. Although the plate-to-grid capacitance (feedback) is small, the power gain is high, and neutralization is required for complete stability and reduced distortion.

In all linear amplifier systems, the driver output impedance should be very low because of the nonlinear input loading characteristics of the amplifier tube as it approaches maximum power output. The lower the driver amplifier impedance, the smaller will be the effect of the nonlinear input loading.

4.4.3 Effects of Idling Plate Current

The choice of the bias point for a linear amplifier used in single-sideband service is critical. The plate current at the zero-signal operating point is chosen for the best compromise between zero-signal plate dissipation and low intermodulation distortion. The bias point establishes the operating point on the tube transfer curve. The effect upon distortion of the operating point was discussed earlier in Section 4.3.2. Intermodulation distortion test data for the EIMAC 4CX1500B is shown in Figure 45. This illustration is a plot of intermodulation distortion and peak envelope output power as a function of zero-signal plate current (I_{bo}). Typically, the zero-signal plate current for minimum distortion will produce about two-thirds of the rated plate dissipation.

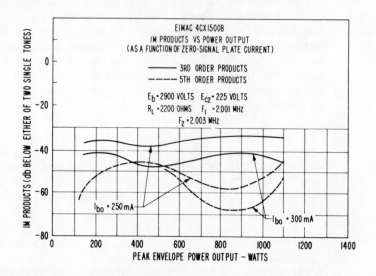

Figure 45. IM Distortion Test Data for EIMAC 4CX1500B
($E_c2 = 225V$)

4.4.4   Effects of Screen Voltage

Choice of screen voltage is a compromise between power output, zero-signal plate current, and intermodulation distortion. Usually, the lowest value of d-c screen voltage compatible with a given power output will produce the lowest intermodulation distortion. Figures 45 and 46 show a comparison of the effects of screen voltage on distortion products for the EIMAC 4CX1500B.

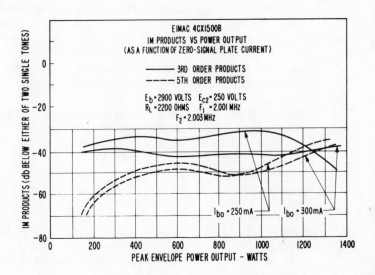

Figure 46. IM Distortion Test Data for EIMAC 4CX1500B
($E_c2 = 250V$)

4.4.5   Grid Driven Linear Amplifiers

The tetrode or pentode linear amplifier is usually grid driven in order to take advantage of the inherent high gain of the tube. A grid-driven amplifier can be driven into the grid current region under proper circumstances. In any case, the input circuit will be loaded by the tube grid. The no-grid-current case will have the input conductance loading, while the grid-current case will have this degree of loading plus grid-current loading. It is therefore desirable (and necessary in the grid-current case) to swamp the input circuit with an appropriate noninductive resistor. The resistor will maintain an almost constant load on the driver and minimize the effects of any nonlinearity in grid loading.

4.4.6   Cathode Driven Linear Amplifiers

The cathode driven amplifier may use either triode, tetrode, or pentode tubes. The drive signal is applied to the cathode in this class of operation. This technique is often referred to as **grounded grid** since the control grid is usually at radio-frequency ground. The cathode-driven amplifier is particularly suitable for high power stages using high-mu triodes in the HF and VHF region. This class of operation normally eliminates the need for neutralization, as the control grid screens the plate from the input circuit. The power gain for suitable triode Class AB cathode-driven amplifiers is in the order of 7 to 20. The actual tube power gain is very nearly the ratio of radio-frequency plate voltage to radio-frequency cathode voltage because the fundamental component of the plate current is common to the input and output circuits.

Tetrode tubes can be used in cathode-driven operation. Power gain is considerably higher than that of triodes, and is in the order of 20 to 50. It is important to recognize that screen-grid current loads the input circuit just as control-grid current does.

For an amplifier located some distance from the driver, an improvement in intermodulation distortion can be realized by tuning the cathode circuit. When the driver is located very close to the amplifier (1/10 wavelength, or so) other means may be used to minimize the nonlinear loading of the cathode-driven stage.

4.5   ADJUSTING AND MONITORING THE LINEAR AMPLIFIER

The individual tube data sheet includes all the necessary parameters required to make first approximation adjustments for optimum linearity. A spectrum analyzer or frequency-tunable voltmeter, in conjunction with a two-tone drive signal, is necessary to make the final adjustments on a linear amplifier. The following procedures may be helpful in setting up a single-sideband linear amplifier and monitoring its operation:

The first step is to apply plate, screen, and suppressor voltages of the recommended values to the pentode linear amplifier and adjust the bias for the specified zero-signal plate current. Once this adjustment is made the operating point has been established.

The second step is to apply single-tone modulation to the amplifier. In a complete transmitter system which includes the audio amplifiers, sideband generator, and interstage amplifiers, the single tone may be obtained from an audio oscillator. For Class AB_1 amplifiers, the drive should be increased until grid current **barely** starts to flow in the stage under test. Next the audio signal is reduced slightly until no current flows. For Class AB_2 amplifiers, the drive should be increased until recommended grid current flows. It will be necessary to resonate the various tuned circuits before the drive is increased to full level. After the drive level has been fixed, the plate loading must be adjusted until recommended single-tone plate current flows (in the case of a triode), or until recommended screen current flows and is obtained (in the case of a tetrode or a pentode).

Note that the above procedure depends upon fixing the zero-signal level point by adjusting the bias and the maximum-signal point with a single-tone test signal. This is an approximate procedure and is useful when only meters and a single-tone test signal are available. A two-tone test signal is required to make meaningful linearity measurements.

4.5.1   Adjustment With Two Tone Drive

Initial adjustments should be made with single-tone drive, as outlined in the previous paragraph, to obtain zero-signal and maximum-signal operating conditions. Once these conditions have been established, the amplifier is then driven with a two-tone test signal **to the same peak grid voltage as that determined for the single-tone case.** The plate current will be considerably less than for the single-tone condition. The ratio of single-tone to two-tone plate current varies between 1.1:1 and 1.57:1. Adjustments in plate loading should not be made before the output of the amplifier has been sampled and observed on a panoramic analyzer or a tunable voltmeter. The actual intermodulation-distortion ratios may be measured and then grid drive and plate loading may be adjusted for minimum distortion compatible with the required peak envelope power output.

4.5.2   Adjusting And Monitoring With Envelope Detectors

In addition to the above methods for adjusting the SSB linear amplifier at maximum-signal level with single-tone modulation and for obtaining optimum linearity with two-tone modulation, it may be convenient to use still another procedure [12] to make linearity adjustments and to provide a means of monitoring transmitted signals.

A pair of envelope detectors in conjunction with an oscilloscope can be employed to observe the linearity of an SSB amplifier regardless of the waveform of the modulating signal. Also, this technique affords instant observation of the effects of amplifier adjustments.

4.5.3   Loading

The r-f plate load of the tube in the linear amplifier has a great effect upon power output and linearity. Once the loading has been adjusted to provide the desired power output and distortion level, it is desirable to have a circuit in the transmitter to continually monitor the loading. A practical circuit should include a system for detecting the input r-f voltage and the output r-f voltage. Then, two detected signals are compared and displayed on a zero-center-scale meter or oscilloscope. With the correct ratio of output to input voltages, there will be no deflection of the meter. Under proper loading adjustment, this condition can be satisfied.

To achieve the proper resistive load to the tube, a method of tuning the plate circuit to the same frequency as the drive signal is required. Such systems have been devised making use of phase detectors. By comparing the phase of the plate voltage to that of the drive signal, one can tell when the plate circuit is resistive. This type of circuit is useful for continuous monitoring while the transmitter is in service. If the plate circuit is off-resonance, the plate load impedance will have a reactive component and hence will create an elliptical operating line. The elliptical operating line reduces efficiency and power output and distorts the linearity characteristic of the stage.

---

12 Pappenfus, et al, op. cit.

NEUTRALIZATION

A completely neutralized amplifier must fulfill two conditions. The first is that the interelectrode capacitance between the input and output circuits be cancelled. The second requirement is that the inductance of the screen grid and cathode assemblies and leads be completely cancelled. Cancellation of these common impedances between the input and output will theoretically prevent oscillation. This also applies in practice, but often not without some difficulty.

There are a variety of methods of accomplishing these ends that will fulfill the two conditions. At frequencies up to about 500 KHz it is not normally necessary to neutralize a grid-driven triode. A grounded-grid cathode-driven triode can usually be operated up into the VHF range without neutralization. Tetrode and pentode amplifiers generally will operate into the HF range without neutralization. As the gain of the amplifier increases, the need to cancel feedback voltage becomes that much more necessary. For this reason, it is usually necessary to neutralize tetrodes and pentodes at the higher frequencies.

5.1 NEUTRALIZATION BELOW VHF

At frequencies below the VHF region, neutralization usually employs a capacitance bridge circuit to balance out the feedback due to the residual plate-to-grid capacitance. This assumes that the screen is well by-passed to ground and so provides the expected screening action. In the VHF and UHF regions the screen is not necessarily at r-f ground potential. The neutralizing circuit, therefore, becomes more involved.

If neutralization on the fundamental frequency below the VHF region is found desirable, normal cross-neutralization of push-pull amplifiers is simplest. The neutralizing capacitors are small. In the case of triodes, special neutralization capacitors are manufactured and are available as catalog items.

In the case of the small tetrode or pentode each capacitor need only be a wire connected to each side of the grid circuit, brought through the chassis deck, and allowed to "look" at the plate of the tube on the opposite half of the circuit. This is illustrated in Figure 47.

Figure 47. Wire neutralizing system.

The wire or rod can be one-half to one inch away from the tube; by adjusting its length or spacing the last trace of coupling can be eliminated from the amplifier. A simple insulating collet mounted on the chassis deck will support the wire or rod and allow it to be adjusted.

5.2   PUSH-PULL NEUTRALIZATION

In the case of a single-ended stage, either a push-pull output or a push-pull input circuit can be used to provide the out-of-phase voltage necessary for neutralization. Because of the lower voltage and the smaller size of the r-f input circuit, it is usually simpler to make the input circuit push-pull and the circuit becomes a "grid-neutralization" circuit (see Figure 48). The neutralizing capacitor, C_n, is small and similar to those described above under cross-neutralization. To maintain the balance of the input circuit while tuning, it is desirable to have a padding capacitor, C_1, equal in size to the input capacitance of the tube.

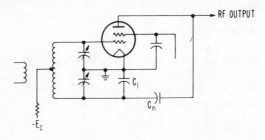

Figure 48.   Push-pull grid neutralization, basic circuit.

5.3   SINGLE-ENDED NEUTRALIZATION

Single-ended tetrode and pentode r-f amplifier stages can also be grid-neutralized without using a conventional push-pull input circuit (see Figure 49). In this method, the input resonant circuit is taken off ground a small amount by making the input circuit by-pass capacitor, C, somewhat smaller than usual. The voltage to ground across the capacitor, C, is out of phase with the grid voltage and can be fed back to the plate to provide neutralization. In this case the neutralizing

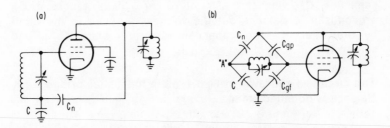

Figure 49.   Single-ended grid neutralization described by Bruene, basic circuit.

capacitor, C_n, is considerably larger than the grid-to-plate capacitor and is about the size of those used for neutralizing triodes.

The basic circuit of this neutralization scheme is shown in Figure 49a. It can be redrawn as a capacitance bridge showing clearly the grid neutralization circuit (see Figure 49b). Balance is obtained when

$$\frac{C_n}{C} = \frac{C_{gp}}{C_{gf}}$$

where C_{gp} is the feedback capacitance grid-to-plate of the tetrode or pentode, the C_{gf} is the total input capacitance, including tube and stray capacitance.

A single-ended amplifier can also be neutralized by taking the plate circuit a small amount off ground as was done in the single-ended grid neutralizing scheme, and by using the tube capacitances as part of the bridge circuit (see Figure 50).

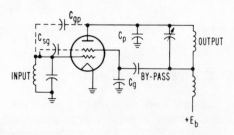

Figure 50. Single-ended plate neutralization, basic circuit.

This circuit differs from the usual r-f amplifier circuit in that the plate by-pass capacitor is returned to the screen side of the screen by-pass capacitor, C_s, and in adding stray capacitance from plate to ground, C_p. The size of screen by-pass capacitor, C_s, and the amount of stray capacitances in C_p are chosen to balance out the voltages induced in the input by the internal tube capacitances grid-to-plate, C_{gp}, and screen to grid, C_{sg}.

The circuit is redrawn in Figure 51 in the usual bridge form. Balance is obtained when

$$\frac{C_p}{C_s} = \frac{C_{gp}}{C_{sg}}$$

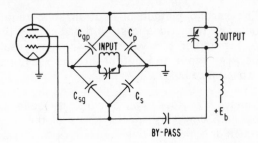

Figure 51. Single-ended plate neutralization showing capacitance bridge circuit present.

In usual tetrode and pentode structures the capacitance from screen-to-grid is roughly half the published tube input capacitance. The tube input capacitance is mainly the sum of the capacitance of the grid-to-screen and the capacitance grid-to-cathode. At first guess these two capacitances are roughly equal, so one is not far off in using half the listed tube input capacitance.

Note that in all neutralizing capacitance bridge circuits, it is assumed that the frequency is low enough so that inductances in the connecting leads and tube structures can be neglected. This is usually not the case in the VHF region, especially in single-ended tetrode and pentode stages where bridge circuits balance with a very small voltage in part of the bridge circuit. At VHF the small amount of voltage developed in the residual inductance of the screen circuit can be enough to accomplish neutralization in itself.

5.4 NEUTRALIZING GROUNDED-GRID AMPLIFIERS

Grounded-grid triode amplifiers offer an attractive alternative to the more usual grid-driven amplifier. The control grid is operated at r-f ground and serves as a shield to capacitive currents from the output to the input circuit. Generally, neutralization is not required until the control grid lead inductive reactance becomes significant. The feedback from the output to the input circuit is no longer due only to the plate-to-filament capacitance. The physical size of the tube and the operating frequency will determine when neutralization is required.

Two methods of neutralization are commonly used with grounded grid amplifiers. In the first method, the grids of a push-pull amplifier are connected to a point having zero impedance to ground, and a bridge of neutralizing capacitances is used which is equal to the plate-filament capacitances of the tubes.

The second method of neutralization requires an inductance between the grid and ground or between the grids of a push-pull amplifier of a value that will compensate for the coupling between input and output circuits resulting from the internal capacitances of the tubes.

Behavior of these two circuits is quite different. They may be considered as special forms of the more general case in which the neutralizing capacitors have values differing from the internal capacitances of the tubes, and in which an appropriate reactance is connected between the grids.

Under these conditions, the value of neutralizing capacitance permits continuous variation of the power amplification, stability, and negative feedback.

The purpose of neutralization is to make the input and output circuits independent of each other with respect to reactive currents. The input current must be independent of the output voltage, and reciprocally. This condition is necessary to permit independent tuning of the input and output circuits, so that the variations in output voltage do not produce variations of phase angle of the input impedance, resulting in phase modulation.

This condition of independence between input and output circuits, which may be called the "neutralized condition," does not necessarily imply stability. This is because the suppression of coupling by capacitive currents between input and output circuits is not sufficient to remove the effect of the output voltage on the cathode-to-grid voltage. A second condition, distinct from neutralization, must be met for complete stability. The effect of the control grid lead inductance must be cancelled.

5.4.1 Symmetrical Grid-Driven Amplifiers

A symmetrical or push-pull grid excited amplifier with grounded cathode is shown in Figure 52. If the inductance of the leads is considered to be negligible at the operating frequency, independence between the input and output circuits is generally obtained by cross-connecting the grids and plates through capacitors C_n having values equal to the internal grid-plate capacitance, C_{gp}, of the vacuum tubes. The requirements of stability and neutralization are fulfilled simultaneously because the input circuit is connected between the grids (in the case of a symmetrical stage) or between the cathode and grid (in a single-ended amplifier).

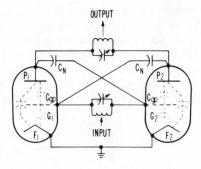

Figure 52. Neutralization of a symmetrical grid-excited
amplifier by cross-connected capacitors.

4.2 Symmetrical Cathode-Driven Amplifiers

The same method of neutralization may be applied in symmetrical cathode-driven amplifiers where the grids are grounded and the lead inductances are considered to be negligible at the operating frequency. The grids and cathodes are inverted and the neutralizing capacitors, C_n, have a value equal to the internal cathode-plate capacitance, C_{fp}, of the vacuum tubes as shown in Figure 53.

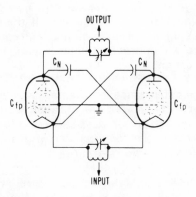

Figure 53. Neutralization by cross-connected capacitors
of a symmetrical cathode-excited amplifier
with grounded grids.

If the grids are not at ground potential because the inductance of the leads is not negligible, coupling may exist between the input and output circuits through the plate-grid capacitances, cathode-grid capacitances, and grid-to-grid inductance. One method of reducing this coupling is to insert between the grids, a series tuned circuit which has zero reactance at the operating frequency as shown in Figure 54.

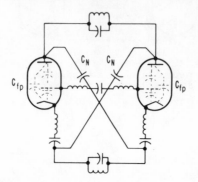

Figure 54. Neutralization by cross-connected capacitors of a symmetrical cathode-excited amplifier with compensation of lead inductance.

The neutralization scheme just described is useful only for the case where no grid current flows. If grid current flows, a grid resistance will appear in parallel with the grid-to-filament capacitance. If the resistance is small in comparison to the reactance of this grid-to-filament capacitance, phase modulation will be produced.

Another important property of the preceding neutralizing method is that power amplification is a function of the neutralizing capacitance while the independence of cathode and plate circuits from the viewpoint of reactive currents may be obtained with any value of neutralizing capacitance. If the neutralizing capacitance is less than the plate-to-filament capacitance of the tube, the stage will operate with low excitation power and high power amplification.

If the neutralizing capacitance is greater than the plate-to-filament capacitance, the power amplification would be quite low, but the total output power possible would be increased. A more complete discussion of grounded-grid amplifier neutralization can be found in the references.[12, 13]

13 "The Inverted Amplifier," C. E. Strong, Elect. Comm., V. 19, No. 3, 1941.

14 "Cathode Excited Linear Amplifiers," J. J. Muller, Elect. Comm., V. 23, 1946.

5.4.3 Grounded-Grid Amplifiers with Grid Impedance

In the special case for the grounded-grid amplifier having a grid impedance and the reactive currents neutralized, the following equations and Figure 55 apply.

$$C_n = C_{fp} - \frac{C_{fg}}{\mu}$$

$$Z_g = - \frac{1}{\left[j\omega \; C_{fg} + C_{gp} \; (1 + \mu) \right]}$$

If in solving the equation for C_n the sign is negative, this indicates in-phase neutralization is required. Conversely, if the sign of C_n is positive, then out-of-phase neutralization is required.

A negative value of Z_g indicates capacitive reactance required and a positive value requires an inductive reactance to be used.

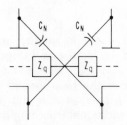

Figure 55. Circuit of grounded-grid amplifier having grid impedance and neutralized for reactive currents.

5.5 NEUTRALIZATION PROCEDURE

5.5.1 Breaking D-C Current Path

The first step to roughly adjust the neutralization is to break the d-c connections of the plate voltage and screen voltage leaving the r-f circuits intact. If the d-c current path is not broken, some current can flow in either one of these circuits even though the voltages are zero. The presence of this current causes the amplifier to work in the normal manner, generating r-f power in the plate circuit. It will then be incorrect to adjust for zero power in the plate circuit. Sufficient r-f grid drive must be applied to provide some grid current or to cause a sensitive r-f meter coupled to the plate to give an indication of feed through power. When the plate circuit is tuned through resonance, the grid current will dip when the circuit is out of neutralization or the r-f meter will peak. The neutralization adjustments are made until the indication is minimum.

5.5.2 Feeding the Grid Circuit

Another very powerful tool for roughly neutralizing the amplifier is to feed the output from a signal generator into the grid circuit. A sensitive r-f detector is inserted between the output connector and the load. The neutralization can then be adjusted for minimum feed through. This technique is very useful in working with the prototype equipment. Actual quantitative measurements can be made. If the insertion loss of the amplifier is less than the expected gain, oscillation will occur. Circuit modification can be made until the isolation is sufficient to warrant a test with high voltages applied. The advantages of this "cold" system: (a) no components are subjected to unusual stress if the amplifier is unstable, and (b) safer, more convenient circuit modifications may be made.

5.5.3 Final Trimming

For the final trimming of the neutralization adjustment, the stage should be returned to operating condition at reduced power similar to that used when testing for parasitic oscillations, or under the final loaded operating conditions. At the higher frequencies and in the VHF region, it will be found that a small additional trimming adjustment of the neutralizing circuit is usually required. When the plate circuit is tuned through resonance, the minimum plate current and maximum control grid current should occur simultaneously. In the case of the tetrode and pentode the d-c screen current should be maximum at the same time.

The neutralizing procedures indicated above apply not only to the HF radio frequencies, but also apply in the VHF or UHF regions. In the latter cases the neutralizing circuit is different and the conventional cross-neutralization schemes may not apply.

As the radio frequency is increased, the reactance of the screen lead inductance of a tetrode or pentode no longer is negligible.

5.5.4 Feedback Circuits in Tetrodes and Pentodes

Careful analysis of the feedback circuits of tetrodes in the VHF region has been made and the basic concepts follow.

The same analysis applies to a pentode. In Figure 56 the tetrode circuit elements involved in the feedback circuits are indicated. These circuit elements are inherent and involve the residual capacitance plate-to-grid, the capacitance from plate-to-screen, the capacitance from screen-to-grid, and the inductance of the screen lead to the tube. It will be noted that the r-f voltage developed in the plate circuit E_p causes a current, I, to flow through the plate-to-screen capacitance, C_{ps}, and the inductance, L, in the screen leads. The passage of this current through the inductance L develops a voltage $-E$ which has a polarity opposite to that of the plate voltage, E_p.

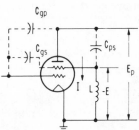

Figure 56. Tetrode characteristics involved in feedback circuit.

In Figure 57 the same circuit elements and voltages have been arranged with a graphical representation where the height above or below the zero line represents magnitude and polarity of the r-f voltage of that part of the circuit with respect to zero. Because all of the circuit components involved are pure reactances, the voltages are either in phase or out of phase, and so can be represented as positive and negative with respect to each other. The voltages plotted are the components only of the r-f output circuit voltage, E_p, and no

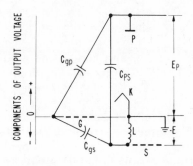

Figure 57. Graphical presentation of components of output circuit voltages in tetrode when self neutralized.

attempt is made to show the normal driving voltage on the grid. The plate "P" is shown at a high positive potential above zero and the magnitude is represented by the distance above the zero line as shown by the dimension, E_p. The voltage developed in the screen lead inductance places the screen at a negative voltage with respect to the plate voltage. The screen of the tube, S, is shown to be below the filament line, or negative, by the amount -E. If the circuit were perfectly neutralized, the control grid, G, would lie on the zero potential line or a filament potential insofar as any action of the r-f plate voltage, E_p, on the input circuit is concerned. If there is no component of output voltage developed between grid and filament, the circuit is neutralized.

The total r-f voltage between plate and screen comprises plate voltage and screen lead inductance voltage -E. This total voltage is applied across a potential divider consisting of the capacitance grid-to-plate, C_{gp}, in series with the capacitance grid-to-screen, C_{gs}. When this potential divider is suitably matched to the magnitudes of the voltage, E_p, and screen lead voltage, -E, the control grid will have no voltage difference to filament as a result of the output circuit voltage, E_p.

5.6   SELF-NEUTRALIZING FREQUENCIES OF TETRODES AND PENTODES

It should be noted in Figure 57 that the potential dividing action between capacitances plate-to-grid, C_{pg}, and grid-to-screen, C_{gs}, will not be affected by the operating frequency. It should also be noted that the division of voltage between plate and screen and screen and ground due to the charging current, I, will vary greatly with frequency. There will, therefore, be some particular frequency at which this potential dividing circuit places the grid at filament potential as far as the plate circuit action is concerned, and this is called the **self-neutralizing frequency** of the tetrode. At this particular frequency the tetrode, or pentode, is inherently neutralized due to the circuit elements within the tube structure and any external added screen lead inductance to ground. Typical self-neutralizing frequencies with normal screen bypassing are as follows:

APPROXIMATE SELF-NEUTRALIZING FREQUENCIES
OF SOME EIMAC TETRODES AND PENTODES

TUBE TYPE	SOCKET	FREQUENCY (MHz)
4-1000A		25 - 30
4-400A		45 - 50
4-250A	(SEE NOTE)	45 - 50
4X500F		75 - 90
4-125A		75 - 90
4-65A		80 - 120
4X150A	SK-600	535 - 540
4CX250B	SK-600	545 - 555
4CX250R	SK-600	565 - 570
4CX350A	SK-600	460 - 470
4CX1000K	SK-820	385 - 395
4CX1000A	SK-810	380 - 390
4CX1500B	SK-810	380 - 390
4CX3000A	SK-1400A	125 - 130
4CX5000A	SK-300A	140 - 170
4CX15,000A	SK-300A	120 - 150
5CX1500A	SK-840	115 - 120
5CX1500A	SK-840*	190 - 300
*Air holes screened.		

Note: Sockets are not called out for these tubes because the recommended sockets do not contain integral bypass capacitors. In these cases, bypass consideration depends on the individual circuit designer.

5.6.1 Operation Below Self-Neutralizing Frequency

When the tube is operated below the self-neutralizing frequency, the normal cross-neutralization circuits apply in this case, a neutralizing capacitor approximately equal to the plate-to-grid capacitance of the tube brings voltage of opposite polarity from the output circuit to the grid, or from the input circuit to the plate.

5.6.2 Operation Above Self-Neutralizing Frequency

If the operating frequency is higher than the self-neutralizing frequency of the tetrode or pentode, the voltage, -E, developed in the screen lead inductance is too large to give the proper voltage division between the internal capacitances of

91

the tube. One obvious method of reducing the voltage in the screen lead reactance is to adjust the inductive reactance of the screen lead to ground so as to lower the total reactance. This takes the form of a series variable capacitor as shown in the graphical representation in Figure 58.

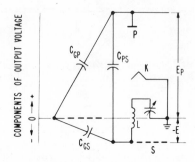

Figure 58. Components of output voltage of a tetrode when neutralized by added series screen-lead capacitance.

Another method would be to change the potential divider network made up of the tube capacitance. This could be done by adding capacitance external to the tube between grid and plate. The method is shown in Figure 58A.This added capacitance plate-to-grid is on the same order of size as the residual grid-to-plate capacitance of the tube and, hence, is similar in construction to the neutralizing capacitance used at a lower frequency. However, in this case, the small wire or rod standing up beside the tube "looking" at the plate (and so forming a neutralizing capacitor) is connected to the grid of the tube rather than to an opposite polarity in the input circuit.

If the r-f power amplifier is operating above the self-neutralizing frequency of the tube and must be tuned over a range of frequencies, it is probably easier to use the screen series tuning capacitor method and make this control available to the operator. If operation is desired over a range of frequencies including the self-neutralizing frequency of the tube, this circuit is also desirable because the incidental lead inductance in the variable tuning capacitor lowers the self-neutralizing frequency of the circuit so that the neutralizing series capacitor can be made to operate over the total desired frequency range. Obviously, if the range is too great, switching of neutralizing circuits will be required. A small 50 to 100 pF variable capacitor in the screen lead has been found to be satisfactory.

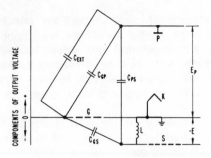

Figure 58A. Components of output voltage of a tetrode when neutralized by added external grid-to-plate capacitance

Another method of changing the self-neutralizing frequency of a tetrode or pentode is obtained when using the general by-passing arrangement of the screen and the filament shown in Figure 59. The screen lead by-passed with minimum inductance to the filament terminal of the tube. Some inductance is introduced in the common filament and screen grounding lead.

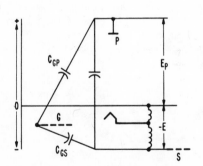

Figure 59. Components of output voltage of a tetrode neutralized by adding inductance common to screen and cathode return.

The grid is shown below the zero voltage or chassis potential, indicating that the voltage developed in the total screen lead inductance to chassis is excessive. If now the filament is tapped up on this inductance, a point can be found where the voltage difference between grid and filament is zero as far as the components of plate voltage are concerned. The arrangement will be found to self-neutralize at a higher frequency than if the filament and screen were separately bypassed to the chassis. Thus, by increasing the self-neutralizing frequency of the tube and screen by-pass arrangement, the tendency of the VHF parasitic to occur is reduced.

If now the frequency of the VHF parasitic is reduced by increasing the inductance of the plate lead (presuming this is the principle frequency defining circuit), it can be made to approach the self-neutralizing frequency of the tube and so suppress the parasitic.

SECTION 6
OPERATING CONDITIONS
FOR VARIOUS APPLICATIONS

6.1   ADJUSTMENT OF LOADING AND EXCITATION

In a typical transformer-coupled audio amplifier, the plate-to-plate load impedance required is given in the technical data sheet for the tube type under consideration or can be calculated. The secondary load impedance is normally defined by the application. It only remains to specify the turns ratio of the transformer.

Once the proper output transformer and secondary load are adjusted, the proper excitation is determined by the plate current. If a means is available to measure the grid voltage swing, this can also be used to indicate proper excitation.

In adjusting tetrode or pentode r-f amplifier for proper excitation and loading, it will be noticed that the procedure is different, depending upon whether the screen voltage is taken from a fixed supply or a dropping resistor supply with poor regulation. In the case where both the screen supply and grid bias are from fixed sources with good regulation, the plate current is almost entirely controlled by the r-f excitation. One should first vary excitation until the desired plate current flows. The loading is then varied until the maximum power output is obtained. Following these adjustments the excitation is then trimmed along with the loading until the desired control grid, and screen grid currents are obtained.

In the case of an r-f amplifier where both the screen and grid bias are taken from sources with poor regulation, the stage will tune very much like a triode r-f power amplifier. The plate current will be adjusted principally by varying the loading, and the excitation will be trimmed to give the desired control grid current. In this case the screen current will be almost entirely set by the choice of the dropping resistor. It will be found that excitation and loading will vary the screen voltage considerably and these should be trimmed to give about normal screen voltage.

The grounded-grid amplifier has been used for many years, but with the advent of new high power "zero bias" triodes it has become more common. To adjust the excitation and loading of a grounded-grid r-f amplifier requires a slightly different procedure. A means of monitoring power output is usually necessary. The plate voltage (plate and screen voltage in the case of a tetrode or pentode) must be applied before the excitation. If this precaution is not followed, there is a very good chance of damage being done to the control grid. The loading is increased as the excitation is increased. When the desired plate current is reached the power output should be noted. The loading can be reduced slightly and the excitation increased until the plate current is the same as before.

If the power output is less than before, a check can be made with increased loading and less excitation. By proper trimming the proper grid current, plate current and optimum power output can be attained.

In a grounded-grid circuit the cathode, or input circuit, is in series with the plate circuit. Because of this, any change made in the plate circuit will have an effect on the input circuit. Therefore, the driver amplifier does not see its designed load until the driven stage is up to full plate current.

6.2   OPERATING VOLTAGES AND CURRENTS

The simplest way to get an idea of the capabilities of the tube, and the voltages and currents to be used on the various electrodes, is to refer to the technical data sheet for that tube type. A number of typical operating conditions are given for various classes of service. A great many other operating conditions are possible, but those in the data sheet are selected to show the maximum capabilities of the tube for different plate voltages. At no time should the maximum ratings for that class of service be exceeded.

As long as none of the maximum ratings of the tube are exceeded, a wide choice of voltages on the plate, screen, or grid is available and a wide range of plate current values may be chosen.

In referring to the characteristic curves of a tube type, it should be recognized that these curves are typical of a normal tube. As in all manufactured products, some tolerance is allowed. For all tube types manufactured there is an established test specification giving the most important parameter ranges used for the quality control of the product.

6.3 EFFECT OF DIFFERENT SCREEN VOLTAGES

Typical operating values for a tetrode or pentode for a particular value of screen voltage are given on the published technical data sheet. The screen voltage is not critical for most applications and the value used has been chosen as a convenient value consistent with low driving power and reasonable screen dissipation. If lower values of screen voltage are used, more driving voltage will be required on the grid to obtain the same plate current. If higher values of screen voltage are used less driving voltage will be required. Thus, high power gain can be had provided the circuit has adequate stability. Care should be observed that the screen dissipation limit is not exceeded. The value of screen voltage can be chosen to suit available power supplies or amplifier conditions.

The published characteristic curves of tetrodes and pentodes are shown for the commonly used screen voltages. Occasionally it is desirable to operate the tetrode or pentode at some screen voltage other than that shown on the characteristic curves. It is a relatively simple matter to convert the published curves to corresponding curves at a different screen voltage by the method to be described.

This conversion method is based on the fact that if all interelectrode voltages are either raised or lowered by the same relative amount, the shape of the voltage field pattern is not altered, nor will the current distribution be altered. The current lines will simply take on new proportionate values in accordance with the three halves power law. The method fails only where insufficient cathode emission or high secondary emission affects the current values.

6.4 THE THREE HALVES POWER LAW

For instance, if the characteristic curves are shown at a screen voltage of 250 volts and it is desired to determine conditions at 500 screen volts, all voltage scales should be multiplied by the same factor that is applied to the screen voltage (in this case, 2). The 1000 volt plate voltage line now becomes 2000 volts, the 50 volt grid voltage line 100 volts, etc.

The current lines then all assume new values in accordance with the 3/2 power law. Since the voltage was increased by a factor of 2, the current lines will all be increased in value by a factor of $2^{3/2}$ or 2.8. Then all the current values should be multiplied by the factor 2.8. The 100 mA line becomes a 280 mA line, etc.

Likewise, if the screen voltage given on the characteristic curve is higher than the conditions desired, the voltage should all be reduced by the same factor that is used to obtain the desired screen voltage. Correspondingly, the current values will all be reduced by an amount equal to the 3/2 power of this factor.

For convenience the 3/2 power of commonly used factors is given in Figure 60.

Voltage Factor	Current Factor
0.25	0.125
0.50	0.35
0.75	0.65
1.00	1.00
1.25	1.40
1.50	1.84
1.75	2.30
2.00	2.80
2.25	3.40
2.50	4.00
2.75	4.60
3.00	5.20

Figure 60. Three-halves power of commonly-used factors.

6.5 BALANCE OF AMPLIFIERS

6.5.1 Push-Pull Amplifiers

In a push-pull r-f amplifier lack of balance of plate circuit or plate dissipation is usually due to lack of symmetry in the r-f circuit. Normally, the tubes are similar enough that such unbalance is not associated with the tube and its characteristics. This point can readily be checked by interchanging the tubes in the sockets (provided both tubes have common d-c voltages to plate, screen, and grid), and observing whether the unbalanced condition remains with the socket location or moves with the tube. If it remains with the socket location, the circuit requires adjustment. If appreciable unbalance is associated with the tube, it is possible that one tube is not normal and should be investigated further.

The basic indicators of balance are the plate current per tube and the plate dissipation of each tube. It is assumed that the circuit applies the same d-c plate voltage, d-c screen voltage (if a tetrode or pentode), and d-c grid bias to each tube from common supplies. Also, it is initially assumed that the plate circuit is mechanically and electrically symmetrical or approximately so.

Unbalance in a push-pull r-f amplifier is usually caused by unequal r-f voltages applied to the grids of the tubes, or by the r-f plate circuit applying unequal r-f voltages to the plates of the tubes. The r-f grid excitation should first be balanced until equal d-c plate currents flow in each tube. Then the r-f plate circuit should be balanced until equal plate dissipation appears on each tube, or equal r-f plate voltage.

The balance of plate current is a more important criterion than equality of screen current (in a tetrode or pentode) or grid current. This results from the fact that tubes tend to be more uniform in plate current characteristics. However, the screen current is very sensitive to lack of voltage balance in the r-f plate circuit and may be used as an indicator.

Once the d-c plate currents per tube have been made equal by adjusting the r-f grid circuit, the r-f plate circuit can be adjusted to give equal plate dissipations. Or, if the tetrodes or pentodes have equal screen current characteristics, the r-f plate circuit could be balanced until equal screen currents results. If the tubes differ somewhat in screen current characteristics, and the circuit has common d-c supply voltages, the final trimming of the plate circuit balance may be made by interchanging tubes and adjusting the circuit to give the same screen current for each tube regardless of its location.

Note that the d-c grid current has not been used as an indicator of balance of the r-f power amplifier. It is probable that after following the foregoing procedure the grid currents will be fairly well balanced, but this condition in itself is not a safe indicator of balance of grid excitation.

6.5.2 Parallel Tube Amplifiers

The previous discussion has been oriented toward the r-f push-pull amplifier. The same comments can be directed to parallel tube r-f amplifiers. The problem of balance to be certain each tube carries its fair share of the load must still be considered.

In audio power amplifiers operating in Class $-AB_1$ or Class $-AB_2$ the idle d-c plate current per tube should be balanced by separate bias adjustments for each tube. In many cases some lack of balance of the plate currents will have negligible effect on the overall performance of the amplifier.

When tubes are operating in the idle position close to cut-off, operation is in a region where the plate current cannot be held to a close percentage tolerance. At this point the action of the plate and screen voltages is in delicate balance with the opposing negative grid voltage. The state of balance is indicated by the plate current. Very minor variations of individual grid wires or diameter of grid wires can upset the balance, and it is practically impossible to control such minor variations in manufacture. In many audio amplifier applications, especially where the larger power tetrodes are used, the circuit should be designed to permit the bias to be adjusted individually on the tubes.

6.6 HARMONIC AMPLIFIER AND CONTROL OF HARMONICS

A pulse of plate current delivered by the tube to the output circuit contains components of the fundamental and most harmonic frequencies. To generate output power that is a harmonic of the exciting voltage applied to the control grid, it is merely necessary to resonate the plate circuit to the desired harmonic frequency. To optimize the performance of the amplifier, it is necessary to adjust the angle of plate current flow to maximize the desired harmonic. The shorter the length of the current pulse in the case of a particular harmonic, the higher will be the plate efficiency; but the bias, exciting voltage, and driving power are increased. Also, if the pulse is too long or too short, the output power drops off appreciably.

The harmonic power output that is obtainable decreases with the order of the harmonic. The relative harmonic output obtainable from a given tube compared with normal Class C output with the same peak space current is approximately inversely proportional to the order of the harmonic. The table given in Figure 61 may be used to estimate performance of a harmonic amplifier.

HARMONIC	Optimum Length of pulse, electrical degrees at the fundamental frequency	Approximate Power output assuming that normal Class C output is 1.0
2	90-120	0.65
3	80-120	0.40
4	70-90	0.30
5	60-72	0.25

Figure 61. Plate-Current Pulse Length and Power Output of Harmonic Amplifiers.

The "Tube Performance Computer" described in Section 3 may be used to estimate the harmonic amplifier performance for tetrodes and pentodes because plate voltage has only a small effect on plate current. It has been found that the plate circuit efficiency of tetrode and pentode harmonic amplifiers is quite high. In triode amplifiers, if feedback of the output harmonic occurs, the phase of the voltage feedback usually reduces the harmonic content of the plate pulse, and thereby lowers the plate circuit efficiency. Since tetrodes and pentodes have negligible feedback, the efficiency of a harmonic amplifier is usually comparable to that of other amplifiers.

Also, the high amplification factor of a tetrode or pentode causes the plate voltage to have little effect on the flow of plate current, and it is easier to obtain plate pulses with high harmonic energies without using excessive grid bias. A well designed tetrode or pentode also permits large r-f voltages to be developed in the plate circuit while still passing high peaks of plate current in the r-f pulse. These two factors help further to increase the plate efficiency.

The previous discussion of harmonics has been for the case where harmonic power in the load has been the objective. The generation and radiation of harmonic energy must be kept to a minimum in a fundamental frequency r-f amplifier.

It is not generally appreciated that the pulse of grid current also contains energy on the harmonic frequencies and control of these harmonic energies may be quite important. The ability of the tetrode and pentode to isolate the output circuit from the input circuit over a very wide range of frequencies is important in avoiding feed-through of harmonic voltages from the grid circuit. An important part of this shielding is the fact that properly designed tetrodes and pentodes permit the construction of complete shielding in the amplifier layout so that coupling external to the tube is also prevented.

In r-f amplifiers operating either on the fundamental or a desired harmonic frequency, the control of unwanted harmonics is very important. The following steps permit reduction of the unwanted harmonic energies present in the output circuit:

(a) The circuit impedance between plate and cathode should be very low for the high harmonic frequencies. This may be obtained by having some or all of the tuning capacitance of the resonant circuit close to the tube.

(b) Complete shielding of the input and output compartments.

(c) The use of inductive output coupling from the resonant plate circuit and possibly a capacitive or Faraday shield between the coupling coil and the tank coil, or a high frequency attenuating circuit such as a Pi, or Pi-L network.

(d) The use of low pass filters for all supply leads and wires coming into the output and input compartments.

(e) The use of resonant traps for particular frequencies.

(f) The use of a low pass filter in series with the output transmission line.

6.7   SHIELDING

In an r-f amplifier the shielding between the input and output circuits must be considered. Triode amplifiers are more tolerant of poor shielding because power gain is relatively low. If the circuit layout is reasonable and no inductive coupling is allowed to exist, quite often the triode amplifier can be built without shielding and it will perform adequately. It would be better engineering practice to shield the input and output circuits. Even if the shielding is not necessary to prevent fundamental frequency oscillation, it will most certainly aid in eliminating any tendency toward parasitic oscillation. The higher the gain of an amplifier the more important the shielding.

6.7.1 Pierced Shields

Tetrode and pentode amplifiers require excellent shielding to prevent input to output circuit coupling. It is advisable to use non-magnetic materials such as copper, aluminum, or brass in the r-f fields to provide the shielding. Quite often a shield must have holes through it to allow the passage of cooling air. In the LF and part of the HF range, the presence of small holes will not impair the shielding. As the frequency is increased the r-f currents flowing around the hole in one compartment cause fields to pass through the hole. Currents are, therefore, induced on the shield in the other compartment. This type of problem can be eliminated by using holes which have significant length. A piece of pipe with a favorable length to diameter ratio as compared to the frequency of operation will act as a "waveguide beyond cutoff attenuator."[15] If more than one hole is required to pass air, a material resembling a honeycomb may be used. The material is commercially available* and provides excellent isolation with a minimum air pressure drop. Several sockets manufactured by EIMAC have this waveguide beyond cutoff air path. These sockets allow the tube in the amplifier to operate at very high gain and up through VHF.

6.7.2 Metal Base Shells and Submounted Sockets

Some tetrodes and pentodes have metal base shells. The shell should be grounded by the clips provided with the socket. This completes the shielding between the output and input circuits since the base shell of the tube comes up opposite the screen shield within the tube itself.

Some pentodes use this metal base shell as the terminal for the suppressor grid. If the suppressor is to be at some potential other than ground, then the base shell must not be d-c grounded. The base shell would be bypassed to ground for r-f and insulated from ground for d-c.

There is a family of tetrodes and pentodes without the metal base shell. It is good practice for this type of tube structure to submount the socket so that the internal screen shield

---

[15] Simon Ramo and John R. Whinnery "Fields and Waves in Modern Radio," New York, Wiley, 1953.

* Hexcel Products, Inc., 2332 Fourth Street, Berkeley, California.

is at the same level as the chassis deck. This technique will improve the input to output circuit shielding. It is very important in submounting a tube that adequate clearance be provided around the base of the tube for passage of cooling air.

6.7.3 Compartments

By placing the tube and circuits in completely enclosed compartments and by properly filtering incoming supply wires, it is possible to prevent coupling out of radio frequency energy by means other than the desired output coupling.

Such filtering prevents the coupling out of energy which may be radiated or be fed back to the input or earlier stages to cause trouble. Energy fed back to the input circuit causes undesirable interaction in tuning, or self-oscillation. If energy is fed back to the earlier stages, the trouble may be greater due to the larger power gain over several stages.

Audio amplifiers using high gain tubes require similar layout consideration. Quite often in the design of an r-f amplifier doors or removable panels must be used. The problem of making a good, low resistance joint at the discontinuity must be met. There are several materials available commercially for this application. Finger stock † has been used for many years. "Teknit" ‡ is also a practical solution. Sometimes it is found that after the wiring has been completed, further shielding of a wire is required. There are various types of shielding tapes § that can be wound on as a temporary or even permanent solution.

6.8 DRIVE POWER REQUIREMENTS

The technical data sheet for a particular tube gives the approximate drive power required. As the frequency of operation increases and the physical size of the tube structure becomes large with respect to this frequency, the drive power requirement will also increase.

---

† Finger stock is manufactured by: EIMAC-Division of Varian, San Carlos, California, 94070; Instrument Specialties Co., Inc., Little Falls, New Jersey; Braun Tool & Instrument Co., Inc., 140 Fifth Avenue, Hawthorne, New Jersey.

‡ "Teknit" is manufactured by: Technical Wire Products, Inc., 129 Dermody Street, Cranford, New Jersey.

§ Magnetic Shield Division, Perfection Mica Co., 1322 North Elston Avenue, Chicago, Illinois.

The drive power requirements of a grounded-cathode amplifier consists of six major parts:

(a) The power consumed by the bias source.

$$P_1 = \text{Ic1 Ec1}$$

(b) The power dissipated in the grid due to rectified grid current.

$$P_2 = \text{Ic1 } e_{cmp}$$

(c) The power consumed in the tuned grid circuit.

$$P_3 = i^2_{c_{rms}} R_{rf}$$

(d) The power loss due to transit time.

$$P_4 = \left(\frac{e_{c_{rms}}}{R_t}\right)^2$$

Where R_t is that part of the resistive component of the tube input impedance due to transit time.

$$R_t = \frac{1}{Kg_m f^2 T^2}$$

(e) The power consumed in that part of the resistive component of the input impedance due to the cathode lead inductance.

$$P_5 = \frac{e_g^2}{R_s}$$

Input resistance resulting from the inductance of the cathode lead equals

$$R_s = \frac{1}{\omega^2 g_m L_k C_{gk}}$$

(f) Power dissipated in the tube envelope due to dielectric loss.

$$P_6 = 1.41 f E_1^2 \epsilon$$

$Ic1$	=	d-c grid current
$Ec1$	=	d-c grid voltage
e_{cmp}	=	maximum positive grid voltage
$i_{c_{rms}}$	=	r.m.s. value of r-f grid current
R_{rf}	=	r-f resistance of grid circuit
e_{crms}	=	r.m.s. value of r-f grid voltage
R_t	=	resistance due to transit time loading
K	=	a constant function of tube geometry
g_m	=	transconductance
f	=	frequency, in hertz
T	=	transit time, cathode to grid
R_s	=	cathode lead inductance input resistance loading
ω	=	$2\pi f$
L_k	=	cathode lead inductance in henries
C_{gk}	=	grid to cathode capacitance in farads
E_1	=	voltage gradient in kilovolts per inch, r.m.s.
ϵ	=	loss factor of dielectric materials

The total driving power in the VHF and UHF region is often greater than the grid dissipation capability of the tube.

6.9 VHF AND UHF OPERATING CONDITIONS FOR SATISFACTORY PLATE EFFICIENCY AND MINIMUM DRIVE

When operating a tube in the VHF and UHF region the driving power can usually be minimized without appreciably affecting the plate conversion efficiency, by the following steps:

(a)   A minimum d-c control grid bias should be used. Frequently, it is advisable to bring this down to approximately cut-off.

(b)   A high value of d-c screen voltage is advisable even though it appears to increase the fraction of the cycle during which plate current flows.

(c)   Using the minimum r-f excitation voltage necessary to obtain plate circuit performance, even though the d-c grid current is considerably lower than one would expect at lower frequencies.

(d)   The cathode lead inductance to the output and input circuits should be kept to a low value. This can be accomplished by using short and wide straps, by using two separate return paths for the input and output circuits or by proper choice of cathode by-pass capacitor.

It has been found that the choice of driving conditions as indicated does not necessarily decrease the plate efficiency as much as at lower radio frequencies. The steps indicated should be tried experimentally to determine whether or not the plate circuit efficiency is appreciably affected. It is preferable to sacrifice plate efficiency somewhat and improve the life expectancy of the tube in the VHF and UHF region.

Optimum output power at these frequencies is obtained when the loading is greater than would be used at lower frequencies. Apparently the use of lower r-f voltage in the plate circuit is desirable. Fortunately, this same condition reduces driving power and screen current (in the tetrode and pentode) and improves life expectancy.

6.10   COOLING TECHNIQUES

Adequate cooling of the tube envelope and seals is one of the principle factors affecting tube life. Deteriorating effects increase directly with the temperature of the tube envelope and seals. The technical data sheet for the particular tube type should be studied thoroughly with reference to the cooling requirements.

Even if no cooling is specified, ample free space for circulation of air around the tube is required or else some air must be forced past the tube.

Excess cooling will have only beneficial results and inadequate cooling is almost certain to invite premature failure of the tube.

Tubes operated in the VHF and UHF region are inherently subjected to greater heating action than tubes operated at lower frequencies. This results directly from the flow of larger r-f charging currents into the tube capacitances, by dielectric losses, and through the tendency of electrons to bombard parts of the tube structure other than the normal grid and plate. Greater cooling is therefore required at these higher frequencies. The technical data sheet for the particular tube type specifies the maximum allowable temperature. For the forced air and water cooled tubes, the recommended amount of air or water is also specified in the technical data sheet. Both the temperature and quantity of coolant should be measured to be certain the cooling is adequate. The problem of making temperature measurements is severe.

6.10.1   Making Temperature Measurements

Thermocouples, contact pyrometers, and other devices sensitive to radiant heat may be used to make temperature measurements, but these devices are often not available or not suited to the particular conditions under which a measurement must be made. For this reason, EIMAC recommends the use of a temperature-sensitive paint such as "Tempilaq," available from local laboratory supply houses in the United States and Canada, and manufactured by the Tempil Division, Big Three Industrial Gas and Equipment Co., Hamilton Blvd., So. Plainfield, New Jersey   07080.

Tempilaq dries to a powdery coat after application. At its critical temperature it melts and virtually disappears. After subsequent cooling it has a crystalline appearance which adequately indicates that the surface with which it is in contact has exceeded the critical temperature. Each sample should be melted on a test piece so that the observer can familiarize himself with the appearance before and after the critical temperature has been passed.

Reliable temperature measurements can be made with Tempilaq provided that it is applied in very thin coats and over small areas of the surface to be measured. The substance as supplied by the manufacturer is too thick for use in the presence of forced-air cooling. It should be thinned, using only the thinner recommended by the manufacturer, and it should be applied with an air brush or atomizer through a paper mask to limit the area covered.

The Tempil Corporation recommends the use of a well-diluted spray of Tempilaq, stating that the amount required to produce a reliable indication is virtually unweighable. This is particularly true when making measurements in the presence of forced-air cooling or on glass envelopes where radiant heat may be intercepted by the Tempilaq itself.

A convenient set of equipment for making measurements with these temperature-sensitive paints is an atomizer with several vials, each equipped with an air-tight cap. One vial may be filled with thinner for cleaning the atomizer, while the remainder may be filled with properly thinned Tempilaq sensitive to several different critical temperatures.

Considering the importance of tube temperatures, every design engineer should familiarize himself with the use of Tempilaq or some other similar substance. Measurements of this kind yield basic information sometimes obtainable in no other way.

Temperature sensitive tapes can also serve to measure temperature. One type called Temp-Plate is available from Williams-Wahl Corp., 1001 Colorado Avenue, Santa Monica, California 90404.

6.10.2 Forced air and convection in cooling

Some of the lower power vacuum tubes may be cooled by normal convection around the base and envelope of the tube. The tube and socket must be mounted in such a position as to allow unobstructed air flow. See Figures 62 and 63.

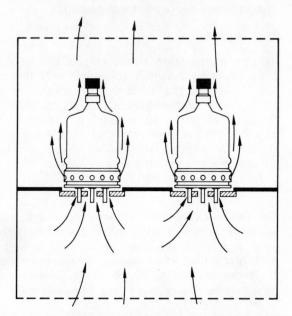

Figure 62. 4-125A mounting providing cooling, shielding and isolation of output and input compartments.

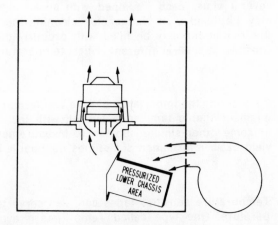

Figure 63. 4CX250B chassis mounting providing cooling, shielding and isolation of output and input compartments.

If the flow of cooling air is upward it will be consistent with the normal flow of convection currents. In all cases the socket is an open structure or has adequate vent holes to allow cooling of the base end of the tube. Cooling air enters through the grid circuit compartment below the socket through a screened opening, passes through the socket to cool the base end of the tube, sweeps upward to cool the envelope and enters the output circuit compartment. The output compartment also has a mesh-covered opening which permits the air to vent out readily. These arrangements apply whether the tube is cooled by forced air or convection circulated air. If the tube is to be forced-air cooled, a suitable fan or blower is used to pressurize the compartment below the tubes. No holes should be provided for the air to pass from the lower to the upper compartment other than the passages through the socket and tube base. Some pressure must be built up to force the proper amount of air through the socket. In the case of convection cooling, open louvers or screened areas permit ready entrance of cool air, and all access holes or vents should have large areas to provide a minimum resistance to the flow of air.

Do not submount a tube so that the chassis deck or mounting deck restricts the flow of air around the base. See Figure 64.

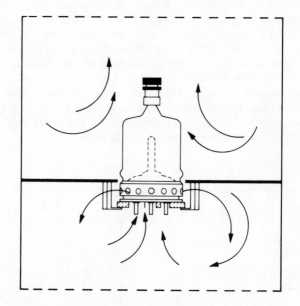

Figure 64. Incorrectly mounted tube. Submounted metal base shell tube prevents effective cooling and does not contribute to shielding.

No improvement in isolating output and input circuits results, and such an arrangement prevents the flow of cooling air, whether forced or by convection currents. If a tube must be recessed into the mounting deck because of space limitations, a recessing cylinder with wide clearances should be used to permit the air from the base holes to vent into the compartment above the deck.

The method of supplying the cooling air to the tube, shown in Figures 62 and 63, has worked successfully, provided the desired flow is obtained. It is preferred over methods which try to force cooling air transversely across the tube base.

In many cases, there are complete air system sockets and chimneys designed specifically for a tube or family of tube types. The technical data sheet specifies the recommended socketing for adequate cooling.

The technical data sheet specifies the back pressure, in inches of water, and the cubic feet per minute required for adequate cooling. In an actual application the back pressure may be measured by means of a simple manometer. This consists of a simple U-shaped glass tube partially filled with water (see Figure 65), which is very useful in measuring low pressure values in connection with air flow. If an air pressure (P) of low value is introduced by connecting the air hose to the left branch of the U, the value of this pressure in inches of water column may be determined by measuring the height (h) between the two water levels. Forced-air cooling systems are capable of removing approximately 50 watts per square centimeter of effective internal anode area.

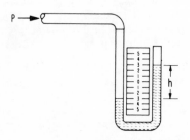

Figure 65. Measuring back-pressure.

6.10.3 Use of Cooling Airflow Data

EIMAC graphically presents minimum cooling airflow requirements for its large external anode tubes in the form of Total Power Dissipated in watts/Tube Temperature Rise in degrees Centigrade ($P_t/\Delta T$) **versus** Mass Airflow Rate in pounds of air per minute (M). These graphs are used in calculating the cooling requirements listed in the data sheets and copies are available from EIMAC.

The graphs apply to a specified tube and socket-chimney combination; further, the direction of airflow is specified. When reverse airflow, i.e., anode-to-base, is to be used, cooling requirements are sharply increased. This is because the air applied to the base seals has already been heated by its passage through the anode cooler, losing much of its cooling effectiveness.

The procedure for using these graphs to determine the minimum cooling requirements is presented in the following:

(a) The total power dissipated (P_t) is determined by adding all of the power dissipated by the tube during operation in its particular installation. This includes plate and filament dissipations plus maximum anticipated grid and screen dissipations where applicable.

Example

Plate Dissipation	5000 watts
Filament Dissipation	350
Screen Dissipation	100
Grid Dissipation	50
Total Dissipation (P_t):	5500 watts

(b) The tube-temperature rise (ΔT) is found by taking the difference between the maximum-rated tube temperature specified in the appropriate data sheet and the maximum air inlet temperature expected.

Example
Assume maximum tube temperature rating = 250°C
Expected maximum cooling air inlet temperature = 50°C
Safety margin = 25°C (advisable; not required but recommended)
$\Delta T = 250 - (50 + 25) = 175$°C
Thus: $P_t/\Delta T = 5500/175 = 31.4$

(c) From EXAMPLE Cooling Airflow Requirements shown in Figure 66, $P_t/\Delta T = 31.4 \rightarrow 7.9$ lbs/min mass airflow rate. This is the mass airflow rate required at any altitude and for the given inlet air temperature to assure a maximum tube temperature of 225°C (250°C rating, minus 25°C safety factor) when the tube is dissipating a total of 5500 watts. Volumetric airflow requirements, however, vary with altitude and inlet air temperature.

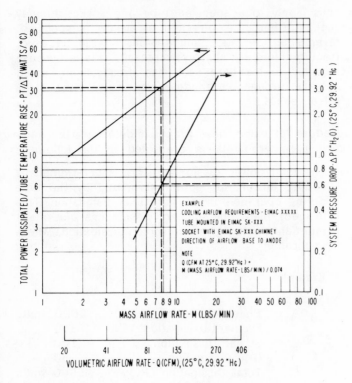

Figure 66. Cooling Airflow Requirements.

(d) To convert the mass airflow rate M (lbs/min) to volumetric airflow rate Q (cfm) at 25°C and at sea level, divide the mass airflow rate by the density of air at 25°C and 29.92 inches Hg. Note that density of air = 0.737 x "Hg÷(273 + °C)lbs/ft³.

Example
Density (25°C, 29.92 "Hg) = 0.737 (29.92)/(273 + 25) = 0.074 lbs/ft³
Q = 7.9/0.074 = 106.8 CFM (25°C, 29.92 "Hg)

(e) The curve on the right side of the graph in Figure 66 is the pressure drop (ΔP) in inches of H_2O across the tube and its specified socket-chimney combination, and is valid at **25°C at sea level only.**

Example
Q = 106.8 CFM (7.9 lbs/min $\rightarrow$ ΔP = 0.61 "H_2O (25°C, 29.92 "Hg)

(f) To adjust the 25°C sea-level laboratory test conditions to any other atmospheric (socket-inlet) condition, multiply both the Q and ΔP values by the ratio of this laboratory standard density (0.074 lbs/ft^3; 25°C at sea level) to the density at the new socket-inlet condition.

Examples
(1) The installation requirements for the EXAMPLE tube with 50°C socket inlet air and at sea level (29.92 "Hg) are:
Density (50°C, 29.92 "Hg) = 0.737 x (29.92)/(273 + 50) = 0.0683 lbs/ft^3
Density ratio = 0.074/0.0683 = 1.032
Q = 1.082 x 106.8 = 115.5 CFM
ΔP = 1.082 x 0.61 = 0.66 "H_2O

(2) The installation requirements for the EXAMPLE tube with 25°C socket inlet air and at 10,000 feet (20.58 "Hg) are:
Density (25°C, 20.58 "Hg) = 0.737 x (20.58)/(273 + 25) = 0.0508 lbs/ft
Density ratio = 0.074/0.0508 = 1.455
Q = 1.455 x 106.8 = 155.5 CFM
ΔP = 1.455 x 0.61 = 0.89 "H_2O

(3) The installation requirements for the EXAMPLE tube with 50°C socket inlet air and at 10,000 feet (20.58 "Hg) are:
Density (50°C, 20.58 "Hg) = 0.737 x (20.58)/(273 + 50) = 0.0469 lbs/ft^3
Density ratio = 0.074/0.0469 = 1.578
Q = 1.578 x 106.8 = 168.5 CFM
ΔP = 1.578 x 0.61 = 0.96 "H_2O

115

(g) A shorter method may be used to correct the 25°C sea-level requirements to both a different temperature and/or barometric socket inlet condition.

These corrections are made by multiplying the Q and ΔP values (determined in Steps 1 through 5) by the appropriate correction factors listed below:

Socket Inlet Air Temperature (°C)	Q and ΔP Correction Factor
0	0.917
5	0.933
10	0.950
15	0.967
20	0.983
25	1.000
30	1.017
35	1.034
40	1.051
45	1.067
50	1.084

Socket Inlet Air Pressure ("Hg)	Altitude (Ft)	Q and ΔP Correction Factor
29.92	0	1.00
24.90	5,000	1.20
20.58	10,000	1.46
16.89	15,000	1.77
13.75	20,000	2.17
11.10	25,000	2.69
8.89	30,000	3.37
7.04	35,000	4.25

Example

The installation requirements for the EXAMPLE tube with 50°C socket inlet air and at 10,000 feet (20.58 "Hg) are:

$Q = 1.084 \times 1.46 \times 106.8 = 168.5$ CFM

$\Delta P = 1.084 \times 1.46 \times 0.61 = 0.96$ "H_2O

(h)   Figure 67 is a graph of the combined correction factors that can be applied to the 25°C sea-level information for land-based installations located at elevations up to 10,000 feet, and for socket-inlet air temperatures between 10°C and 50°C.

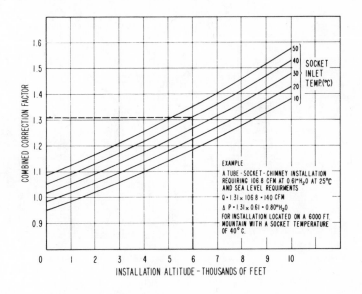

Figure 67. Combined correction factors for land-based installations.

Example

The installation requirements for the EXAMPLE tube with 50°C socket inlet air at 10,000 feet are:

$Q = 1.579 \times 106.8 = 168.5$ CFM

$\Delta P = 1.579 \times 0.61 = 0.96$ "H_2O

Good engineering judgment must be used when applying altitude and temperature corrections to the 25°C sea-level cooling requirements for airborne installations. Although the air outside the aircraft

117

may be very cold at high altitudes, the air actually entering the tube socket may be many degrees warmer. This inlet temperature (and pressure) is affected by each installation design (compressed, ram, static, or recirculating air in a pressurized heat exchanger).

Figure 68 is a convenient curve used to convert Mass Airflow Rate (lbs/min) into volumetric airflow rate (cfm) at 25°C and sea-level.

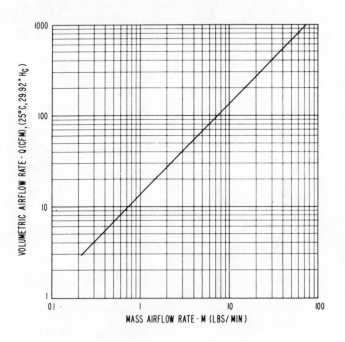

Figure 68. Conversion of mass airflow rate to volumetric airflow rate.

6.10.4 Blower Selection for Elevated Tube Installations

In the section immediately preceding, a method of determining minimum air-cooling requirements for external anode tubes was described, pertaining to any altitude and air temperature. Since most blower manufacturers furnish catalog data on their products in the form of volumetric airflow, Q (cfm) versus Operating Back Pressure, ΔP (inches of water) for **sea level conditions only**, the information gained by the foregoing procedure cannot be compared directly with the data furnished by the blower manufacturers, for the purpose of selecting the proper blower. The following method is recommended for use in selecting a blower for altitude applications from existing blower catalog data:

(a) Determine the Q and ΔP requirements for the tube-socket-chimney combination for an ambient air temperature of 25°C at sea level. Include estimated ΔP of duct and filter.

(b) The system's corrected Q and ΔP requirements for the actual inlet temperature and altitude conditions are determined by multiplying by the correction factor shown in Figure 67

(c) Again multiply the ΔP, but not the Q, requirement by the correction factor cited in Step b.

(d) The corrected Q factor and doubly-corrected ΔP value are then used to select a blower from the manufacturer's published sea-level curves. Although this blower will overcool the tube at sea level when operated in an ambient temperature of 25°C, it will provide adequate cooling at the actual inlet temperature and altitude conditions.

An example:

Given: A tube-socket-chimney requires 100 CFM at 1.0" H_2O at 25°C and sea level. (Normally determined as per step a).

Required: Determine the requirements for selecting a blower from manufacturer's catalog data (25°C, Sea Level Conditions) to insure that the system is adequately cooled in a 40°C ambient air temperature at an altitude of 8000 feet.

Solution: Step 1) - Given

Step 2) - From Fig. 67, it is determined that the correction factor for a combined environment of 8000 feet altitude at 40°C inlet temperature is 1.42.

119

The corrected Q and ΔP is then,

$Q = 1.42 \times 100 = 142$ CFM

$\Delta P = 1.42 \times 1.0 = 1.42'' H_2O$

Step 3) - The doubly corrected ΔP is then,

$\Delta P = 1.42 \times 1.42 = 2.02 '' H_2O$

Step 4) - The blower selected from the manufacturer's catalog must be capable of delivering 142 CFM at 2.02 "H_2O in an ambient temperature of 25°C at sea level in order that the tube-socket-chimney system will be supplied with 142 CFM at 1.42 "H_2O at 40°C and 8000 feet.

For further information pertaining to sub-critical air flow through an orifice, refer to MARKS' ENGINEER'S HANDBOOK, 5th edition, pg. 334.

6.10.5 Water Cooling

Water-cooled tubes depend upon an adequate flow of water to carry away heat fast enough to maintain the cooled parts at a safe operating temperature. The recommended flow as specified by the technical data sheet should be maintained at all times when the tube is in operation. Inadequate flow of water at high temperature may cause formation of steam bubbles at the anode surface where the water is in direct contact with it. This can contribute to premature tube failure.

By electrolysis and scale formation, hard water may cause a gradual constriction of some part of the water system. Therefore, water flow and plumbing fittings must be inspected regularly. The fittings on the positive potential end of an insulating section of hose or ceramic water coil or column are particularly subject to corrosion or electrolysis unless they have protective "targets." Targets should be checked periodically and replaced when they have disintegrated.

Cooling water temperature is important. The tube technical data sheet should be consulted to be sure operation is within safe limits.

Purity of cooling water is important. The specific resistivity must be maintained at 1 megohm-cm minimum at 25°C. Distilled or deionized water should be used and the purity and flow protection should be periodically checked to insure against excessive degradation. Oxygen and carbon dioxide in the coolant will form copper oxide reducing cooling efficiency and electrolysis may destroy the coolant passages. In addition, a filter screen should be installed in the tube inlet line to trap any circulating debris which might clog coolant passages within the tube.

If the air is humid and the cooling water is cold, condensation accumulates on the surfaces of all pipes, tube jackets and other parts carrying water. This condensation may decrease surface leakage resistance, or drops of water may fall on some electrical component and cause erratic operation or failure. Some means is then necessary to control the temperature of the incoming water to keep it above the dew point. Control is rather easy in a closed cooling system, but in a system which employs tap water and drains the exhaust water into a sewer, control is difficult.

Connecting lines should be of an insulating material such as polypropylene, but chlorinated polyvinyl chloride (CPVC) is also acceptable and is stronger.

Circulating water can remove about 1000 watts per square centimeter of effective internal anode area. In practice, the temperature of water leaving the tube is limited to 70°C to preclude the possibility of spot boiling. This water is then passed through a heat exchanger where it is cooled to 30°C-40°C before being pumped over the tube anode again.

Refer to the EIMAC Application Bulletin 16 for additional details concerning liquid cooling systems.

6.10.6 Vapor-Phase Cooling

Vapor-phase cooling offers some advantages over water cooling systems by exploiting the latent heat of the evaporation of water. Raising the temperature of one gram of water from 40°C to 70°C (as in a water system) requires 30 calories of energy. **Transforming one gram of water at 100°C to steam vapor requires 540 calories.** In a vapor-cooling system, then, a given quantity of water will remove nearly twenty times as much energy as in a water-cooling system. Power densities as high as 135 watts per square centimeter of effective internal anode surface have been attained through vapor cooling.

A typical vapor-phase installation consists of a tube with a specially designed anode immersed in a "boiler" filled with distilled water. When power is applied to the tube, anode dissipation heats the water to 100°C; further applied energy causes the water to boil and be converted into steam vapor. The vapor is passed through a condenser where it gives up its energy and is converted back into the liquid state. This condensate is then returned to the boiler, completing the cycle. The result is a system that reduces the water flow requirement nearly 20 times and due to the thermosyphoning action which results in a natural circulation of the water, eliminates the need for the pump required in a circulating water system. A bonus effect of vapor cooling is almost complete silence during operation.

A dramatic improvement over water-cooling systems is a reduction in the size of the condenser required. A condenser of any given thermal capacity can be reduced in size if the mean temperature gradient (Δ Tm) between the cooled liquid and the secondary coolant can be increased. In a practical water-cooling system like the one just described, water enters the heat exchanger at 70°C and leaves at about 40°C, the mean temperature being 55°C. With air as a secondary coolant (or heat sink) at about 30°C, there is a mean temperature differential, Δ Tm, of 25°C. In a typical vapor cooling system, vapor enters the condenser at 100°C, and water leaves at 100°C, resulting in a mean temperature of 100°C. The mean temperature differential Δ Tm then between the steam-water and air is now 100°C — 25°C = 75°C, or **three times that of the water-cooled system.** Tests at EIMAC have confirmed this and have shown that heat exchanger equipment for a vapor-cooled system will require only about one-third to one-quarter the capacity associated with water-cooling systems.

Where air-cooled condensers are preferred, this higher thermal gradient can be exploited in reducing the size of condenser equipment and in lowering the blower horsepower requirement. In some instances where sufficient area is available, natural convection alone is used to cool the steam condensers, resulting in complete elimination of the condenser blower.

Where water is preferred as the secondary coolant, similar ratios apply and water consumption is drastically reduced. For example, a water cooling system at the 100 kW dissipation level will require about 100 cubic feet of secondary water per hour, or 500,000 cubic feet over 5000 hours. With vapor-cooling, this is reduced to one-third, a savings of 333,333 cubic feet. With a water cost of $1.50 per 1000 cubic feet, about $500 in water cost alone is saved over a 5000 hour period. In addition, a five-horsepower pump is eliminated. This pump requires about 25,000 kWhr of electrical power over the same period, at a cost of about $375. Thus the vapor-cooling system would save the user about $875 in operating costs over a 5000 hour period.

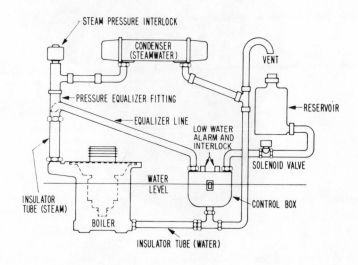

Figure 69. Typical vapor-phase cooling system.

(1) INSTALLATION NOTES

A typical EIMAC vapor-phase cooling system is shown in Figure 69. It consists of the power tube, boiler, condenser, insulating tubing, control box, reservoir, and associated plumbing. Detailed installation suggestions for the various components are discussed below.

Boiler—The boiler supports the power tube and contains the water used for cooling. In addition, it acts as the high voltage anode connector. The boiler should be mounted so that the axis of the tube is vertical. For effective cooling, the tilt should be limited to less than 2° to insure that the anode is covered with water and the steam outlet is clear.

Figure 70. 4CV35,000A tetrode mounted in BR-200 boiler.

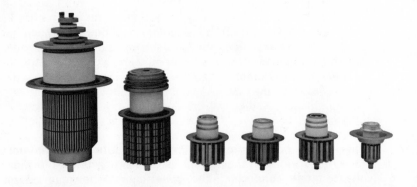

Figure 71. EIMAC vapor-cooled tubes for mounting in EIMAC Boilers.

Figure 70 shows an EIMAC 4CV35, 000A tetrode mounted in a BR-200 boiler. Other EIMAC tubes designed for vapor phase cooling systems are shown in Figure 71.

The tube's anode flange must seal securely against the O-ring provided on the boiler. A locking flange presses the anode flange against the O-ring for a vapor-tight seal. The steam outlet at the top of the steam separation chamber on the boiler and the water inlet at the bottom of the boiler are equipped with fittings for attaching the pyrex insulating tubing. A "target" to inhibit electrolytic action is provided in the inlet water fitting.

Since in most cases the boiler is at high potential relative to ground, it must be electrically insulated from the rest of the system. It should be mounted on insulators and the steam and water connections should be made through pyrex insulating tubing. Boilers can be constructed with provisions for mounting two or three tubes in parallel. These would contain single water inlet and steam outlet fittings.

Insulating Tubing—Length of the steam and water insulating lines will vary with individual installation requirements, but will always be shorter than would be needed in a circulating-water system. The length of the insulating tubing is dependent on the voltage to be applied, the purity of the water, and the volume of returned cooling water. In the vapor-cooling system, water is constantly being re-distilled, there is a minimum of contamination, and only pure distilled water is introduced into the boiler. In addition, the water inlet line is of smaller diameter—because of the low water flow rate—and has inherently higher resistance. Therefore, a two-foot section of pyrex tubing has the capability of preventing voltage flashover up to 20kV, and will also have negligible leakage current. Because of the excellent insulating properties of steam (and the purity of any condensate) the outlet steam line can be made equally short.

Control Box—The function of the control box is to monitor and control the water level in the boiler. A typical box is shown in Figure 72.

Figure 72. CB-202 control box.

The control box also serves as a partial reservoir, and is an air-tight vessel containing an overflow siphon and two float switches. When the water level drops approximately 1/4" below the recommended level, the first switch is closed. It may at the same time be used to activate a solenoid-controlled water valve to admit more distilled water from an external reservoir, and/or actuate a warning alarm.

The second float switch is operated if and when the water level should drop approximately 1/2" below the optimum level. This would be tantamount to a water failure, and the switch would be used to open the control circuit interlocks and remove tube power.

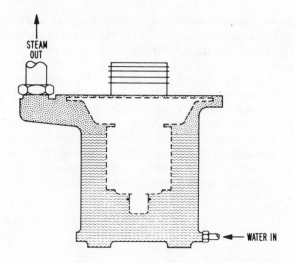

Figure 73. Cutaway of "classic" boiler and tube combination (BR-101 boiler and 4CV8000A tetrode).

For the control box to perform its protective function properly, its water level mark must be precisely level with the water level mark on the boiler. For electrical reasons, the control box will generally be mounted some distance from the boiler, and therefore leveling of the two components should be carefully checked during installation. Figure 73 shows a cutaway drawing of a "classic" boiler and tube combination, and Figure 74 is a cutaway drawing of a control box, showing the position of the float switches and the overflow pipe.

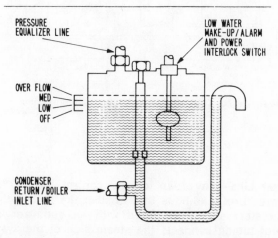

Figure 74. Cutaway view of EIMAC Control Box showing position of float switches and overflow pipe.

The control box also serves a secondary function as a reservoir. During extended operation, some quantity of water and steam is being circulated through the condenser, and some will be lost through the air vent. The amount is, of course, dependent on the size of the system. The water level in the boiler will gradually drop. The use of the control box as a reservoir minimizes this effect. In large or multiple-tube installations, the use of an auxiliary reservoir connected to the control box is recommended to increase the ratio of stored water to circulating water and steam. Where it may be necessary to operate multiple tubes at different physical elevations, individual control boxes are required. A multiple-tube system is shown in Figure 75.

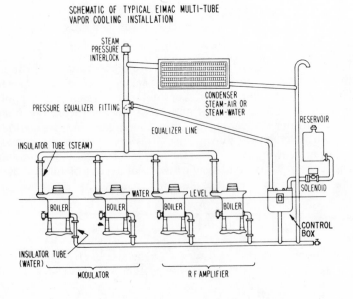

Figure 75. Typical 4-tube vapor cooling system with common water supply.

Equalizer Line—In order for the control box to "see" the same pressure conditions that exist in the boiler, the vapor-phase system should be fitted with an equalizer line. This length of tubing connects the steam side of the system with the top of the control box. As a partial steam pressure begins to build up in the boiler, the equalizer line allows this same pressure to appear in the control box. Steam pressure is low—less than 0.5 psi above atmosphere—but would introduce error in the control box water level unless equalized.

The fitting used to connect the equalizer line to the steam outlet tube must be constructed to prevent a venturi effect from developing because of the velocity of the vapor. This is best accomplished by directing an elbow within the adapter fitting toward the boiler, as shown in Figure 76.

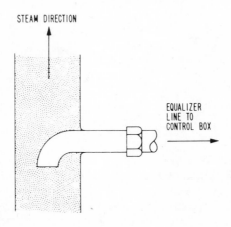

Figure 76. Cutaway of pressure equalizer fitting.

Condensers—Both air-cooled and water-cooled condensers are available for vapor-cooling systems. Condensers should be chosen with good reserve capabilities and low pressure drop. The air-cooled and water-cooled condensers may be mounted in any position, providing they allow the condensed water to flow freely by gravity to the boiler return line. Water must not be allowed to stand in the condenser where it might cause back-pressure to the entering stream.

The condenser should be mounted above the level of the boiler(s) so that water will drain from it to the boiler return line. Where it is necessary to mount the condenser at a lower physical level than the system water level, an auxiliary pump should be used to return water to the boiler. This arrangement is recommended for the "steam-out-the-bottom" boiler system to be discussed later under "Alternate Vapor-cooling Systems." A "steam-out-the-bottom" system is shown in Figure 77.

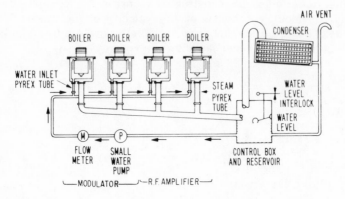

Figure 77. Typical 4-tube system using "steam-out-the-bottom" boilers.

Pressure Interlock—EIMAC suggests the use of a steam pressure interlock switch on the steam or inlet side of the condenser. This switch, set at about 0.5 lbs. per square inch, is used as a power interlock that senses any abnormal steam pressure due to constrictions in the condenser or piping.

Piping—Piping should be of copper or glass throughout the system. The steam piping should be the same diameter as the pyrex tube from the boiler. The size is dependent on power level and the volume of generated steam, and will range from 1-3/4" at the 8 kW level to 6" for the 250 kW level of dissipation. The steam path should be as direct as is practical and must be sloped to prevent condensate from collecting at some low point where it might cause back-pressure. All low spots should be drained back to the inlet water line.

Water return piping from the condenser to the control box will vary from 3/4" to 1-3/4" in diameter, depending again on the power level. This tubing should be the same diameter as the boiler inlet water fitting. It should be sloped so that water or vapor pockets do not exist, and must allow the condensate to return by gravity to the control box and the boiler. A vent to air on the outlet side of the condenser should be incorporated to maintain the water side of the system at atmospheric pressure. Provisions for draining the distilled water should be provided at the system's lowest level.

The equalizer line should also be sloped from the adapter fitting on the steam line to the top of the control box. This will allow the condensate to return to the control box.

Automatic Refilling System—Figures 69 and 75 show typical vapor-cooling systems with provisions to provide additional water to the control box. An auxiliary reservoir is connected through a solenoid-operated water valve to the control box. When accumulated water loss due to evaporation causes the water level in the boiler and the control box to drop about 1/4" below normal, the first float switch in the control box closes and actuates the solenoid-controlled valve to permit makeup water to enter the system. When the proper level is restored, the switch opens, the valve closes, and the flow of makeup water is stopped.

TUBE	TYPE	MAXIMUM PLATE DISSIPATION	BOILER*	CONTROL BOX	PYREX STEAM* TUBE	PYREX WATER* TUBE	PYREX TO* COPPER ADAPTER FITTING	PRESSURE EQUALIZER FITTING
4CV8000A	TETRODE	8 kw	BR-101	CB-102	1¼"	½"	AF-100	AD-100
4CV8000B	TETRODE	8 kw	INTEGRAL	CB-102	1¼"	½"	AF-100	AD-100
4CV20,000A	TETRODE	20 kw	BR-200	CB-202	2½"	½"	AF-200	AD-200
3CV30,000A3	TRIODE	30 kw	BR-200	CB-202	2½"	½"	AF-200	AD-200
4CV35,000A	TETRODE	35 kw	BR-200	CB-202	2½"	½"	AF-200	AD-200
4CV100,000C	TETRODE	100 kw	BR-300 BR-310	CB-202	3½"	¾"	AF-300	AD-300
4CV250,000C	TETRODE	250 kw	BR-600 BR-605	CB-202	6"	1¼"	AF-600	AD-600

*For multiple tube system, these components are multiplied by number of tubes used.

Other Accessories:
1. Air-cooled condenser } EIMAC will quote on
2. Water-cooled condenser } individual requirements
3. Steam Pressure Interlock
4. Solenoid Water Valve
5. Reservoir: RE-100   1 quart
          RE-200   2 quart
          RE-300   1 gallon

6.10.7 Alternate Vapor Cooling Systems

The system described thus far is the so-called "classic" system which consists of a separate tube, boiler, condenser, and level control box. Variations on these schemes are numerous. One such alternate system, offered by EIMAC for use with the larger tubes, uses a "steam-out-the-bottom" boiler. This configuration makes it possible to keep the steam and water systems, plus the plumbing, below the tubes. Figure 77, shows a typical "steam-out-the-bottom" system and Figures 78 and 79 show boilers associated with this particular cooling technique. This approach has the advantages of keeping the plumbing away from the input circuitry.

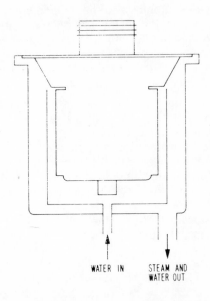

WATER IN   STEAM AND
WATER OUT

Figure 78. Cutaway view of "steam-out-the-bottom" boilers.

A small water pump circulates a continuous flow of water over a weir, or baffle, in the boiler, maintaining a constant water level. Generated steam is forced under slight pressure out of the bottom of the boiler, through an insulator tube in the condenser. Water from the condenser flows into the control box before being pumped back into the boiler. Protective devices must include a water flow interlock and the usual level control in the control box to insure an adequate water supply.

6.10.8 Maintenance

Maintenance problems associated with circulating water systems are practically eliminated through vapor cooling systems. As mentioned earlier, **systems can be designed to eliminate all rotating machinery or moving parts.**

System cleanliness does, however, require periodic attention. The glass insulator tubes should be inspected occasionally to be sure they contain no deposits which might cause voltage flashover. Water conductivity should be checked periodically by measuring the d-c resistance, as in a typical circulating water system. Water should be replaced if its d-c resistance drops below 1,000,000 ohms/cm^2.

In practice, the vapor-cooling system will remain cleaner longer than a water-cooled system. In the vapor-cooled boiler, the water is continually being redistilled and only pure water is introduced at the bottom of the boiler. Any contaminants will tend to remain in the boiler itself, where they can be easily removed. The periods between equipment shutdowns for draining and cleaning will be at least twice as long for the vapor-cooling system because of this inherent self-cleaning action.

Each time a tube is removed or replaced, the rubber O-ring between the boiler and the tube should be inspected and replaced if necessary. At the same time the inside of the boiler and the control box should be inspected and cleaned if necessary.

The electrolytic target should be replaced whenever its metallic end is no longer visible in the inlet water line.

6.10.9 The Physics of Boiling Water

Design of vapor-phase cooling components such as anodes and boilers are dependent on a thorough understanding of the laws of heat transfer and hydrodynamics. The Nukiyama Curve shown in Figure 81 presents heat-transfer capability (measured in watts/cm²) of a heated surface, submerged in water at various temperatures.

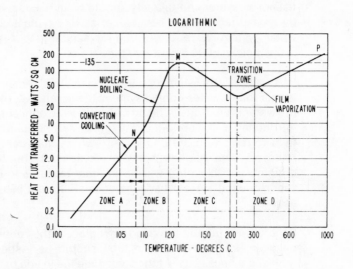

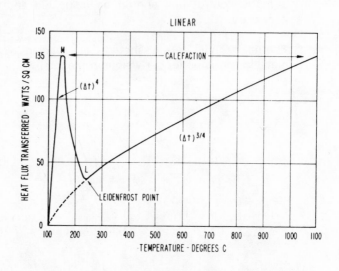

Figure 81. Nukiyama heat transfer curves.

The first portion of the curve—Zone A—indicates that from 100°C to about 108°C, heat transfer is a linear function of temperature differential between the hot surface and the water, reaching a maximum of about five watts per square centimeter at that temperature (Point N). This is the so-called convection-cooling zone. Boiling takes place in the heated water at some point away from the surface.

From 108°C to 125°C—Zone B—heat transfer increases as the fourth power of ΔT until, at 125°C (Point M) it reaches 135 watts/cm^2. This zone is characterized by nucleate boiling; that is, individual bubbles of vapor are formed at the hot surface, break away, and travel upward through the water to the atmosphere.

Above 125°C an unstable portion of the Nukiyama Curve is seen, where increasing the temperature of the heated surface actually reduces the unit thermal conductivity. At this area—Zone C—the vapor partially insulates the heated surface from the water until about 225°C is reached on the hot surface. At this point—called the Leidenfrost point—the surface becomes completely covered with a sheath of vapor and all heat transfer is accomplished through this vapor cover. Thermal conductivity of only 30 watts/cm^2 is realized at the Leidenfrost point, only about one-quarter of the thermal conductivity is realized at Point M (125°C).

From this point on through Zone D, the "film vaporization zone," the heat transfer increases with temperature until at about 1000°C the value of 135 watts/cm^2 is again reached.

The linear plot of the Nukiyama Curve indicates that Zones A and B are relatively narrow areas and that a heated surface with unlimited heat capacity will tend to pass from Zone A to Zone D in a short time. This irreversible super-heating is known as "calefaction." For a cylindrical vacuum tube anode the passing into total calefaction would not be tolerated, as any unit heat transfer density above 135 watts/cm^2 would result in temperatures above 1000°C, well above the safe limits for the tube.

6.10.10 Anode Design for Vapor Cooling

The success of vapor phase cooling is dependent on anode and boiler designs that will allow a tube to operate at a temperature which results in a maximum amount of heat dissipation.

The most common approach has been to incorporate thick, vertical fins on the exterior of the anode to achieve a radial temperature gradient on the surfaces submerged in water.

This way, a "hot spot" does not cause instantaneous runaway of the tube; only the average fin temperature increases and this merely shifts the temperature range to a somewhat higher level. From the graph in Figure 81, it can be seen that the heat flux lost by going from "M" to "L" on the finroot is being gained by moving an equal "temperature distance" to the right at the cooler fin tip. This excess heating is, of course, limited by the maximum temperature on the I. D. of the anode. Usually, the temperatures of the fins vary from approximately 110°C at the tip to approximately 180°C at the root.

Since the average overall fin temperature is approximately 115°C, the average transferred heat flux is approximately 60 watts/cm², as can be seen from Figure 82. Consequently, the external surface should be about five times the internal area in order to reach the 300 watts/cm² capability mentioned earlier.

When operating at low dissipation levels, boiling takes place at the root of the fin. Increasing power density causes this boiling area to move out toward the end of the fin until at rated dissipation levels boiling is taking place on the outer half of the fins. Good design dictates that the anode fin outer edge always remain at less than 125°C.

Anode shape is also important in assuring good cooling, by breaking up the sheath of vapor that might tend to form at the surfaces. To a point, the more complicated the shape, the more efficient is the anode cooler. Often horizontal slots are milled into the vertical fins to provide more area and to break up bubbles. The more vigorous the boiling action, the less is the possibility of forming this insulating vapor sheath. One design — the "pineapple" — carries this idea to the extreme, and incorporates square "knobs" all around the anode to provide dozens of heat radiating surfaces. However, the "finned" anode is generally adequate and is less costly to fabricate.

Another popular anode design for lower power densities up to 100 watts/cm² is the "holed" anode, wherein a heavy cylindrical anode is made with vertical holes in the outside wall. Vapor is formed by the boiling of water within the holes and is siphoned upward through the holes to the top of the boiler. This type of cooler always operates below the calefaction point and is used in smaller tube types.

To aid in heat-transfer calculations, a table of useful conversion factors is presented in Figure 82.

USEFUL CONVERSION FACTORS

ENERGY

BTU	= energy required to raise one pound of water one degree fahrenheit
CALORIE	= energy required to raise one gram of water one degree centigrade
KILOGRAM-CALORIE	= 1000 calories
1 kW	= 3413 Btu/hr
	= 57 Btu/min
	= 860 kg-calories/hr
	= 14.34 kg-calories/min
1 Btu	= 252 calories

BOILING

Latent heat of vaporization (water at atmospheric pressure)	= 540 calories/gram
	= 970 Btu/lb
1 kW dissipation	= 3.53 pounds H_2O/hr at 100°C transformed into steam at 100°C
	= 0.42 gallons/hr
1 cubic foot water	= 62.4 pounds of water
	= 7.48 gallons of water
	= 1600 cubic feet of steam

GENERAL

C	$= \frac{5}{9} (F - 32)$
F	$= \frac{9}{5} C + 32$
1 inch H_2O	= 0.036 psi
	= 0.58 oz/in²
1 inch Hg	= 0.49 psi

Figure 82. Useful conversion factors.

As power tubes become more compact, the problems of removing the heat increase. All of the previously mentioned cooling techniques can and have been used with compact equipment. There are certain applications where conduction cooling is the preferred technique. A typical application of a conduction cooled tube would be in airborne equipment. The skin of the aircraft, or other vehicle, may be used as an infinite heat sink. No pressurization is required as is for convection and forced air cooling. No liquid and associated circulating system is required. Another application is in shipborne equipment. The hull of the ship is a perfect heat sink.

Quite often in mobile and fixed applications it is desirable to conduct all heat in the equipment to one cold plate which can be air or liquid cooled.

Large tubes can use liquid cooled conduction clamps. This technique will permit the replacement of the tube without exposure of the liquid system to the atmosphere.

In conduction cooled power tubes, the cooling system is an integral part of the electrical circuit. The thermal link between the anode and the heat sink can, in certain applications, add to the output capacitance. The method of contacting the base of the tube must satisfy both the electrical and heat transfer requirements.

Figure 83. Different conduction cooled tubes manufactured by EIMAC.

The tubes illustrated in Figure 83 use Beryllium Oxide as the thermal link between the part of the tube to be cooled and the heat sink. Beryllium Oxide is a material that insulates electrically like a ceramic, but conducts heat like a metal. Figure 84 compares the relative thermal conductivities of Beryllium Oxide and some other materials. Figure 85 indicates the variation in properties to be expected with changes in temperature.

Variation of Electrical and Thermal Properties With Temperature—

	20°C	120°C	260°C	400°C	538°C
Thermal Conductivity Heat Transfer in btu/sq ft/ft/hr/°F					
99.5% BeO	140	120	65	50	40
99.5% Al_2O_3	20	17	12	7.5	6
95% Al_2O_3	13.5				
Glass	0.3				
Power Dissipation in watts/cm/°C					
BeO	2.4	2.1	1.1	0.9	0.7
Electrical Resistivity in ohm-cm					
BeO	$>10^{16}$	10^{14}	5×10^{12}	10^{12}	10^{11}
Al_2O_3	10^{14}	10^{14}	10^{12}	10^{12}	10^{11}
Glass	10^{12}	10^{10}	10^{8}	10^{6}	
Dielectric Constant at 8.5 GHz					
BeO	6.57	6.64	6.75	6.90	7.05
Al_2O_3	9.4	9.5	9.6	9.7	9.8
Loss Tangent at 8.5 GHz					
BeO	.00044	.00040	.00040	.00049	.00080

Figure 84. Variation in properties due to changes in temperature.

Relative Thermal Conductivities—
(As Percentage of Thermal Conductivity of Copper)

Silver	105
Copper	100
Berlox high-purity BeO	62
Aluminum	55
Beryllium	39
Molybdenum	39
Steel	9.1
High-purity alumina	7.7
Steatite	0.9
Mica	0.18
Phenolics, epoxies	0.13
Fluorocarbons	0.05

Figure 85. Relative thermal conductivity of BeO.

6.11   TUBE LIFE

6.11.1 Maximum Tube Ratings

The technical data sheet for each tube type gives the basic maximum ratings for each class of service. The data sheet also gives references to the type of cooling required and how much. The maximum temperature permissible for reasonable life is also specified. Careful observance of the information on the data sheet will avoid damage to the tube and shortening of its useful life.

In general, the tube ratings are so chosen that operation within the ratings will give a minimum of 1000 hours of guaranteed life. The typical life expectancy is therefore considerably greater and will depend upon a great many factors. In general, operation below the maximum ratings will increase the life expectancy of the tube. This is especially true with reduction in the plate dissipation of the tube.

If tubes are to be used in pulse service with short pulses and appreciable off-time between pulses, the tube ratings are quite different.

A very large factor in tube life is the temperature of the thoriated-tungsten cathode. The equipment manufacturer and the end user of the equipment have more control over tube life through proper adjustment of filament voltage (filament power) than is generally realized. This is true because tube ratings and equipment designs are conservative in peak cathode emission required of the tube compared with peak cathode emission available at nominal rated filament voltage.

It is good practice to determine, in the field for each particular combination of equipment and operating power level, the nominal filament voltage for best life. This is best done in the field by measuring some important parameter of performance such as plate current, power output, or distortion, while filament voltage on the power tube is reduced. At some point in filament voltage there will be a noticeable reduction in plate current, or power output, or an increase in distortion. Safe operation may be at a filament voltage slightly higher than that point at which performance appeared to deteriorate. A recheck should be made in 12 to 24 hours to make certain the emission is stable.

The thoriated-tungsten filament or cathode is processed in a hydrocarbon atmosphere to form a deep layer of ditungsten carbide on the surface. Stable emission is not possible without the carbide. If the carbide layer is too deep, the filament becomes too brittle to withstand shipping and handling. The end of useful life for this type of filament occurs when most of the carbon has evaporated or combined with residual gas, depleting the carbide surface layer.

Theoretically a 3% increase in filament voltage will result in a 20° Kelvin increase in temperature, a 20% increase in peak emission, and a 50% decrease in life due to carbon loss. This, of course, works the other way, too. For a small decrease in temperature and peak emission, life of the carbide layer and hence tube life can be increased by a substantial percentage. Peak emission as meant here is the emission obtained in the test for emission described in the Test Specification. This is normally many times the peak emission required in communication service.

6.11.2 VHF and UHF Life Considerations

A tube designed for VHF and UHF work must be very small if practical resonant circuits are to be built around them. Furthermore, these tubes operate less efficiently and have much greater incidental losses than at a lower frequency. For these reasons, the power which must be dissipated from the electrodes and tube envelope seals is much greater per unit of area than for tubes designed solely for low frequency.

If the tubes are to become part of a UHF line circuit or cavity UHF circuit, the inductance associated with the electrode supports and leads must be reduced to a very small value. In the case of the 4CPX250K, 4CX250B and 3CX10,000A3 type structures, some of the electrode leads and supports take the form of large surfaces, conical or cylindrical in shape, and extremely short. This means that the amount of heat conducted out through the metal-to-ceramic seals is greatly increased. It also means that the terminal connections of the tube are large surfaces with relatively thin walls.

The mechanical layout of sockets, connections and circuits close to the tube must allow ample cooling air to be blown against the tube seals and surfaces. Also, ample contacting surface must be provided to carry heavy radio frequency charging currents. Since these two requirements may tend to conflict, considerable thought must be given to an adequate layout.

6.11.3 Connectors

Where the tube terminals are large cylindrical surfaces, the contacting portions of the socket are either spring collets or a multiplicity of spring fingers. Usually these multiple contacting surfaces are made of beryllium copper to preserve the spring tension at the relatively high temperatures present on the tube terminals, and are silver plated to reduce r-f resistance.

Rigid clamping connectors should be avoided even though the radius of the curvature seems to be close to that of the cylindrical contacting surface of the tube. It has been found that such rigid clamping connectors will distort the tube terminal and fracture the adjacent seal. Similarly set screw connecting devices are questionable on large cylindrical tube terminals unless they act to distribute the pressure uniformly and without any distorting effects.

If the connectors fail to provide multiple contacts to the cylindrical tube seals, concentration of r-f charging current will result and the local overheating may be destructive. Once the connector loses its spring action the heating is aggravated and damage to the tube is very apt to occur. All tube connectors should be inspected and serviced regularly to be sure that uniform, good contact to the tube results.

It is never advisable to drill holes in any part of the tube structure to provide contact. Many of the metal parts are only 10 to 15 thousandths of an inch thick.

6.11.4 Backheating by Electrons

Another action involving the motion of electrons within the tube is present at VHF and UHF and has been commonly referred to as backheating of the cathode. Due to the fact that the time of flight of the electrons from the cathode through the grid structure to the plate becomes an appreciable part of the cycle, the electrons can be stopped in flight and turned back by the rapidly changing grid voltage. Under these conditions the electrons are turned back or deflected from their normal paths and given excess energy with which the electrons bombard the cathode and other portions of the tube structure. This effect can be greatly aggravated by the choice of operating conditions to the extent that very destructive effects occur. The tube can even be destroyed within a few minutes under severe conditions.

Fortunately, the conditions which tend to minimize this back-bombardment by electrons are the same as those giving minimum driving voltage as discussed under "VHF Operating Conditions." The tendency for electrons to be turned back in flight is reduced by the use of the lowest possible r-f grid voltage on the tube. This is obtained by using the lowest possible d-c grid bias. In tetrodes this effect is inherently much lower because of the action of the d-c accelerating the electrons toward the anode, and also inherently permits the use of much smaller grid voltages. Consequently, under favorable conditions the number of electrons turned back to heat the cathode and tube structure can be kept to a practical low level. In addition to the use of low d-c grid bias, a high screen voltage is desirable.

At the same time, the plate circuit should always operate with heavy loading (low external plate impedance) so that the minimum instantaneous value of plate voltage shall stay sufficiently positive to continue accelerating electrons to the anode. For this reason, best life is had when .the tetrode amplifier is heavily loaded as indicated by having small values of d-c screen and d-c control grid current.

NEVER OPERATE WITH LIGHT PLATE LOADING. If the plate load is removed so that the minimum instantaneous plate voltage tends to fall to values around cathode potential (as it must do when the loading is removed completely and excitation is present), the number of electrons turned back can be completely destructive to the tube. It has been found that under conditions of "no loading" the electron bombardment and increased electric field heating of the insulating portion of the tube is often sufficient to cause a suck-in of the glass, or even cause cracking of a ceramic envelope. Automatic protection should be installed to remove all voltages from the tube when the plate circuit loading becomes too light for the amount of excitation applied.

It should be noted that parasitic oscillations are seldom loaded heavily, as indicated by the high grid currents often had during such self-oscillation. Thus, excessive r-f plate voltages are developed which, at VHF, can be damaging in the same manner as unloaded operation on a VHF fundamental frequency. Should such unloaded VHF parasitic oscillation be present simultaneously with apparently satisfactory operation on the fundamentals, unexplained reduction of life may result.

Occasionally, also, an output line circuit can resonate simultaneously to a harmonic frequency as well as to the fundamental frequency. The higher resonant modes of practical line circuits are not normally harmonically related, but sometimes the tuning curve of a mode will cross the fundamental tuning curve and at that point the circuit will build up resonant voltages at both the harmonic frequency and fundamental frequency. The harmonic resonance is usually lightly loaded and the damaging action is similar to that of lightly loaded parasitic or fundamental operation. Again, the operation of the tube and circuit on the fundamental may appear normal, but with lower than expected efficiency, damaging action can occur to some degree.

In addition to operating the tube with minimum bias, high screen voltage, and heavy loading on the plate circuit, some degree of compensation for the remaining backheating of the cathode may be required. This can be accomplished by lowering the filament voltage or heater voltage until the cathode operates at normal temperature. It has been found with tetrodes and pentodes that by taking precautions necessary to minimize back-bombardment by electrons the compensation for backheating of the cathode is not large and may often be neglected.

END

The following Engineering Newsletters and Application Bulletins may be obtained at no cost by writing to: Application Engineering Dept., EIMAC division of varian, 301 Industrial Way, San Carlos, CA 94070.

Engineering Newsletter   Title

6   Blower Selection for Elevated Tube Installation

8   Cooling, Temperature Measurements With Tempilaq

9   Cooling, Temperature vs Life Expectancy

12   Tube Life vs Filament Voltage

19   Use of Cooling Airflow Data

21   Conditioning of Large Power Tubes

Application Bulletins   Title

5   Tube Performance Computer

16   Water Purity Requirements in Liquid Cooling Systems

17   Fault Protection

18   Water Purity Requirements in Liquid Cooling Systems

Amateur Service Bulletins   Title

AS58 - Transmitting Tubes--How to Use and Abuse Them

AS32 - Forced-air Cooling of Transmitting Tubes

BIBLIOGRAPHY

1. **Radio Engineering,** F. E. Terman, McGraw-Hill.
2. **Hyper and Ultra-High Frequency Engineering,** Sarbacher and Edson, Wiley.
3. **Television Principles,** Dome, McGraw-Hill.
4. **Radio Transmitters,** Gray and Grahm, McGraw-Hill.
5. **Fields and Waves in Modern Radio,** Ramo and Whinnery, Wiley.
6. **Single Sideband Principles and Circuits,** Pappenfus, Bruene and Schoenike, McGraw-Hill.
7. **Forced Air Cooling Primer for the Electronic Engineer,** Henry G. Dietz, The Henry G. Dietz Co., Inc., 12-16 Astoria Blvd., Long Island, New York,
8. **Applied Electronics,** MIT Staff, Wiley.
9. **Thermionic Valves,** A. H. W. Beck, Cambridge.
10. **Materials Technology for Electron Tubes,** Kohl, Reinhold.
11. "The Inverted Amplifier," C. E. Strong, **Electronic Communications,** Vol. 19, No. 3, 1941.
12. "Cathode-Excited Linear Amplifiers," J. J. Muller, **Electronic Communications,** Vol. 23, Sept. 1946.
13. **Radio Engineering Handbook,** Keith Henney, McGraw-Hill.
14. **Pulse Generators,** Glasoe and Lebacqz, Radiation Laboratory Series, Vol. 5, McGraw-Hill.